30 YEARS AGO...

STAR-LORD   GAMORA   ROCKET RACCOON   GROOT   DRAX   IRON MAN

COSMIC AVENGERS

WRITER: **BRIAN MICHAEL BENDIS**

PENCILERS: **STEVE McNIVEN** (#0.1, 1-3) & **SARA PICHELLI** (#2-3)

INKERS: **JOHN DELL** WITH **MARK MORALES** (#2), **STEVE McNIVEN** (#2-3) & **SARA PICHELLI** (#2-3)

COLORIST: **JUSTIN PONSOR**   COVER ART: **STEVE McNIVEN, JOHN DELL** & **JUSTIN PONSOR**

LETTERER: **VC'S CORY PETIT**   ASSISTANT EDITOR: **ELLIE PYLE**   EDITOR: **STEPHEN WACKER**

TOMORROW'S AVENGERS

WRITER: **BRIAN MICHAEL BENDIS**

ART: **MICHAEL AVON OEMING** & **RAIN BEREDO** (DRAX), **MING DOYLE** & **JAVIER RODRIGUEZ** (ROCKET RACCOON) AND **MICHAEL DEL MUNDO** (GAMORA & GROOT)

LAYOUTS (DRAX, ROCKET RACCOON, GAMORA): **YVES BIGEREL**

LETTERER: **VC'S JOE CARAMAGNA**   COVER ART: **MING DOYLE**   EDITOR: **SANA AMANAT**

SENIOR EDITOR: **STEPHEN WACKER**

COLLECTION EDITOR: **JENNIFER GRÜNWALD**   ASSISTANT EDITOR: **SARAH BRUNSTAD**
ASSOCIATE MANAGING EDITOR: **ALEX STARBUCK**   EDITOR, SPECIAL PROJECTS: **MARK D. BEAZLEY**
SENIOR EDITOR, SPECIAL PROJECTS: **JEFF YOUNGQUIST**   SVP PRINT, SALES & MARKETING: **DAVID GABRIEL**
BOOK DESIGNER: **RODOLFO MURAGUCHI**

EDITOR IN CHIEF: **AXEL ALONSO**   CHIEF CREATIVE OFFICER: **JOE QUESADA**
PUBLISHER: **DAN BUCKLEY**   EXECUTIVE PRODUCER: **ALAN FINE**

GUARDIANS OF THE GALAXY VOL. 1: COSMIC AVENGERS. Contains material originally published in magazine form as GUARDIANS OF THE GALAXY #1-3 and #0.1, and GUARDIANS OF THE GALAXY: TOMORROW'S AVENGERS #1. First printing 2014. ISBN# 978-0-7851-9209-1. Published by MARVEL WORLDWIDE, INC., a subsidiary of MARVEL ENTERTAINMENT, LLC. OFFICE OF PUBLICATION: 135 West 50th Street, New York, NY 10020. Copyright © 2013 and 2014 Marvel Characters, Inc. All rights reserved. All characters featured in this issue and the distinctive names and likenesses thereof, and all related indicia are trademarks of Marvel Characters, Inc. No similarity between any of the names, characters, persons, and/or institutions in this magazine with those of any living or dead person or institution is intended, and any such similarity which may exist is purely coincidental. **Printed in the U.S.A.** ALAN FINE, EVP - Office of the President, Marvel Worldwide, Inc. and EVP & CMO Marvel Characters B.V.; DAN BUCKLEY, Publisher & President - Print, Animation & Digital Divisions; JOE QUESADA, Chief Creative Officer; TOM BREVOORT, SVP of Publishing; DAVID BOGART, SVP of Operations & Procurement, Publishing; C.B. CEBULSKI, SVP of Creator & Content Development; DAVID GABRIEL, SVP Print, Sales & Marketing; JIM O'KEEFE, VP of Operations & Logistics; DAN CARR, Executive Director of Publishing Technology; SUSAN CRESPI, Editorial Operations Manager; ALEX MORALES, Publishing Operations Manager; STAN LEE, Chairman Emeritus. For information regarding advertising in Marvel Comics or on Marvel.com, please contact Niza Disla, Director of Marvel Partnerships, at ndisla@marvel.com. For Marvel subscription inquiries, please call 800-217-9158. **Manufactured between 5/21/2014 and 6/14/2014 by R.R. DONNELLEY, INC., SALEM, VA, USA.**

10 9 8 7 6 5 4 3 2 1

DIANS
ALAXY

"NO.

"NO,
MOM.

"HE BROKE UP
WITH *ME!!*"

OH MY GOD! ARE YOU DEAD?

PLEASE DON'T BE DEAD...

ARE YOU AIR FORCE?

I'VE NEVER SEEN A PLANE THAT LOOKS ANYTHING LIKE THIS.

CAN YOU HEAR ME?

OH THANK GOD, YOU'RE ALIVE.

AMERICAN!!

TOTALLY AMERICAN!!

UN-UNLESS YOU'RE NOT-- AMERICAN!!

GREGGER

OKAY, UM, SO HERE'S THE DEAL...

I HAD THE PHONE IN MY HAND. I WAS ABOUT TO CALL THE AUTHORITIES...

BUT THE THING IS I HAVE TRIED SO HARD, FOR MY ENTIRE LIFE, TO JUST LIVE HERE QUIETLY AND DO MY WORK.

AND I DON'T WANT, I MEAN I *REALLY* DON'T WANT, THE NEWS AND THE AIR FORCE AND EVERYONE ELSE ON THE PLANET TO COME HERE AND CAUSE ALL KINDS OF CHAOS AND RIP UP MY PROPERTY AND QUESTION ME--

BUT *YOU* HELD A GUN TO MY HEAD.

YOU SPEAK ENGLISH.

EARTH ENGLISH.

AMERICAN EARTH ENGLISH.

WHERE AM I *EXACTLY*?

UH, COLORADO.

ROCKY MOUNTAIN HIGH.

YOUR MILITARY WOULD NOT BE ABLE TO DETECT MY SHIP'S LANDING.

OKAY, SO, I NEED YOU TO GET YOUR WEIRD SHIP AND I NEED YOU TO GET OFF MY LAND.

CAN YOU DO THAT WITHOUT CAUSING A RUCKUS?

(EARTHER?)

MEREDITH.

FOLLOWED BY WHOM?

THE ATMOSPHERE IS VERY THICK HERE.

UH, WHAT'S YOUR NAME?

EARTH. WAS I FOLLOWED?

FOLLOWED? NO.

OKAY.

I CAN WORK WITH THAT SITUATION.

WHAT IS YOUR NAME, EARTHER?

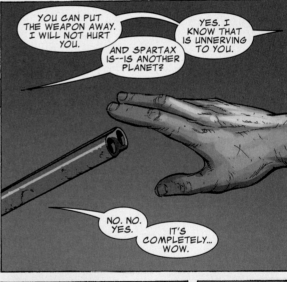

WHAT'S HAPPENING?

IT'S TIME.

FOR?

FOR ME TO RETURN HOME.

THE SHIP IS FIXED?

IT WAS FIXED A FEW OF YOUR DAYS AGO.

I STAYED FOR YOU.

STAY LONGER.

I HAVE TO GO.

I AM NEEDED. THERE IS A WAR.

TAKE ME WITH YOU.

HAVE OUGHT BOUT ELSE.

BUT IT WOULD BE CRUEL AND SELFISH.

BECAUSE?

I AM...MY PEOPLE ARE... FIGHTING A WAR WITH A TERRIBLE ENEMY

YOU WOULD NOT BE SAFE AND I CANNOT PUT YOU IN A SITUATION WHERE I *KNOW* THAT TO BE TRUE.

SO YOU HAVE A *WIFE AND KIDS* ON THAT PLANET OF YOURS.

I DO NOT.

YOU ARE NOT READY FOR-- NO ONE ON EARTH IS READY FOR WHAT IS GOING ON IN THE REST OF THIS GALAXY.

I BADLY WANT TO STAY HERE.

BUT YOU CAN'T.

I WILL TRY TO COME BACK TO YOU.

DO YOU WANT YOUR GUN I HID FROM YOU?

YOU KEEP IT.

HOW ROMANTIC.

IT IS.

IT WAS MADE FOR ME.

THERE IS NO OTHER LIKE IT.

I CAN'T BELIEVE THIS.

PETER QUILL!!

DID YOU DO YOUR MATH HOMEWORK?

I'M TAKIN' A BREAK.

WHAT DID I SAY ABOUT READING THAT CRAP?

IT'S NOT CRAP, MOM.

I'M READING.

THIS IS READING.

THAT IS NOT READING.

YOU SHOULD READ IT. IT'LL BLOW YOUR MIND OUT THROUGH THE TOP OF YOUR HEAD AND THEN IT'LL--

GO FINISH YOUR HOMEWORK.

UGH!!

WHAT DO YOU WANT TO DO LATER?

I'D LIKE TO READ MY COMIC BOOK.

IT'S FRIDAY NIGHT.

WE LIVE 22 MILES FROM ANYTHING AND ANYONE.

WOW.

WHAT?

YOU LOOK JUST LIKE YOUR FATHER, ALL OF A SUDDEN.

IT'S NOT AN INSULT.

I DON'T HAVE A FATHER. YOU *KNOW* I DON'T HAVE A FATHER.

AND YOU KNOW IT UPSETS ME WHEN YOU *SAY THAT!!*

YEAH? WHERE? *WHERE* IS HE?

YOU *DO* HAVE A FATHER.

OH, DAD?

DAD!

STOP IT.

I TOLD YOU TO STOP SAYING THAT.

I *TOLD* YOU!

GOD!

STOP.

WHAT HAPPENED, PETER?

HE WAS PICKING ON A GIRL.

ARE YOU HURT?

NO ONE WAS HELPING.

NO.

GO WASH UP FOR DINNER.

RAIN IS COMING.

THE SPARTAX BLOODLINE WILL NOT CONTINUE.

MOM?

MOMZZ

AAGH!!

HEY!!

WHAT THE HELL?

WHAT THE--?

AGH!

MOM
HAD A--?

WHAT IS
THIS?

MOM!!

GAS
LEAK?

YOU
SHOULD
HAVE
SEEN THE
PLACE.

BAD?

IT'S
KINDLING.

POOR
KID.

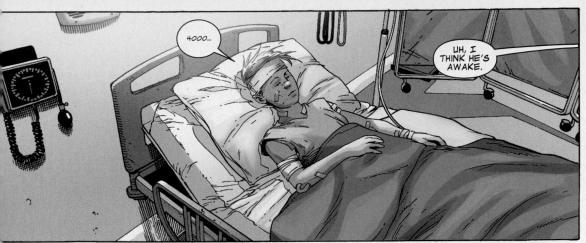

SOMEONE IS GOING TO COME UP AND TALK TO YOU.

I KNOW IT WON'T FEEL LIKE IT BUT YOU ARE A *VERY* LUCKY BOY.

YOU ARE ALIVE.

YOU'RE GETTING A *SECOND CHANCE.*

OH, AND THE PARAMEDICS FOUND YOUR SPACE TOY.

I THOUGHT YOU WOULD WANT IT.

I KNOW IT'S NOT-- IT'S SOMETHING, AT LEAST.

"A LOT OF THIS, OBVIOUSLY, I FOUND OUT AFTER THE FACT.

"BUT THE QUESTION WAS...WHY?

"WHY DID A BUNCH OF ALIENS FLY HALFWAY ACROSS THE GALAXY TO WHACK A 10-YEAR-OLD BOY...?"

IT WAS BECAUSE MY FATHER WAS AND IS SPARTAX ROYALTY.

I WAS THE NEXT IN LINE FOR THE THRONE.

AND I WAS BEQUEATHED THIS ONE OF A KIND WEAPON.

A WEAPON OF THE ELEMENTS.

AS SOON AS THEY HEARD ABOUT ME, THE BADOON CAME TO KILL ME.

FUNNY THING IS-- THEY THOUGHT THEY DID.

THEY THOUGHT I WAS DEAD.

THEY THOUGHT THAT STOPPED THE BLOOD LINE.

I LIVED THE REST OF MY CHILDHOOD IN AN ORPHANAGE AND A COUPLE OF FOSTER HOMES...

...BUT THE SECOND I COULD FIND A WAY OFF PLANET EARTH I TOOK IT.

I JOINED NASA. I DID EVERYTHING.

I GOT UP HERE AND HERE I AM.

THOSE BADOON KILLED MY MOTHER AND TRIED TO KILL ME.

AND MY ASS OF A FATHER DIDN'T DO A DAMN THING ABOUT IT.

SO I THOUGHT TO MYSELF, YOU KNOW, MY IDIOT DAD CAN KEEP ON FIGHTING HIS NEVER ENDING WAR...

...AND THE BADOON CAN GO ON WREAKING HAVOC ALL OVER THE GALAXY...

...BUT I CAN MAKE DAMN WELL SURE THEY NEVER TOUCH EARTH AGAIN.

#0.1 VARIANT BY ED MCGUINNESS & MARTE GRACIA

WHAT EXACTLY DO YOU THINK YOU'RE DOING, MISTER QUILL?

AND, TRUST ME, I KNOW HOW...

YOU...

YOU SHOULD GET OUT OF HERE.

WHAT ARE YOU TALKING ABOUT?

YOU SHOULD GET OUT OF HERE NOW.

EARTH.

WHAT ABOUT IT?

I NEED YOU TO STAY AWAY FROM IT.

I'M SORRY?

I KNOW THIS ISN'T EASY. IT'S YOUR HOME PLANET.

IT IS?

PETER--

OH YEAH, YEAH, I *REMEMBER* NOW.

I REMEMBER YOU CAME TO EARTH, KNOCKED UP MY MOM THEN ABANDONED HER *AND* ME.

PETER.

AND WHY-- WHY DO YOU NEED ME TO STAY AWAY FROM IT?

WHAT ARE YOU UP TO?

I'M TRYING TO SAVE IT.

THIS IS WHY I DON'T EVER WANT TO TALK TO YOU...I DON'T BELIEVE A WORD YOU SAY.

WHAT I AM ABOUT TO TELL YOU ONLY A HANDFUL OF PEOPLE IN THE ENTIRE GALAXY KNOW...

YOU MAKE A LAW THAT SAYS NO ONE IS ALLOWED TO TOUCH THE EARTH AND ALL YOU WILL BE DOING IS PUTTING A GIANT *TARGET* ON IT.

YOU WOULD, LITERALLY, BE *DARING* OTHER EMPIRES, *YOUR* ENEMIES, THE BADOON, THANOS, TO MAKE A GRAB FOR IT.

YOU *KNOW* THAT.

WHAT I KNOW IS: *YOU* ARE THE STAR-LORD OF SPARTAX!

THAT IS YOUR BIRTHRIGHT!

INSTEAD, YOU'RE GALLIVANTING ALL OVER THE GALAXY DOING--!

STOP IT.

TAKE YOUR PLACE AS THE FIRSTBORN OF THE SPARTAX EMPIRE.

UNBELIEVABLE.

YOU'RE THE STAR-LORD. IT'S YOUR BIRTHRIGHT.

LET ME MAKE THIS AS CLEAR AS I CAN...

I DON'T LIKE HOW YOU *MADE* YOUR EMPIRE.

SO I'M *NOT* BECOMING A PRINCE OF YOUR EMPIRE.

THE ANSWER TO YOU ON THIS AND EVERYTHING ELSE IS: *GO KRUTACK YOURSELF.*

I AM YOUR FATHER *AND* YOUR KING!

AND IF I *FIND OUT* YOU ARE PUTTING THE EARTH IN HARM'S WAY JUST SO YOU CAN--

YOU WILL NOT SPEAK TO ME IN--!

CRASSSHHHH

GAMORA, NO!

AR

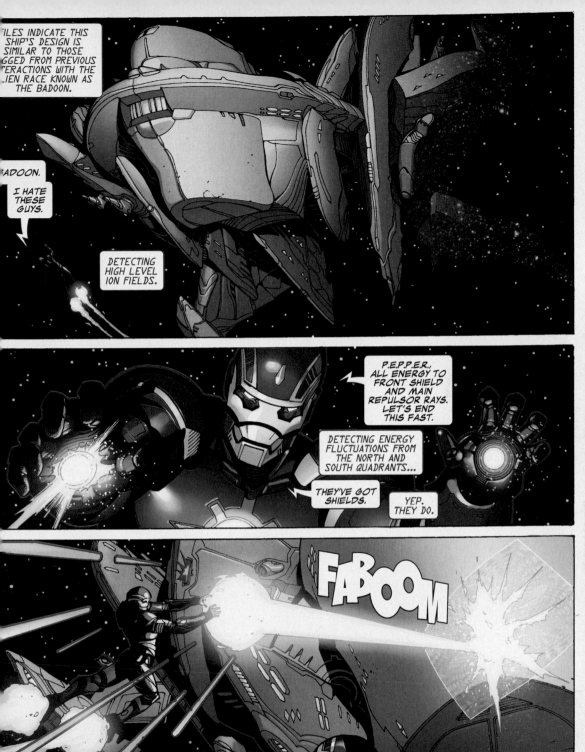

FILES INDICATE THIS SHIP'S DESIGN IS SIMILAR TO THOSE LOGGED FROM PREVIOUS INTERACTIONS WITH THE ALIEN RACE KNOWN AS THE BADOON.

BADOON. I HATE THESE GUYS.

DETECTING HIGH LEVEL ION FIELDS.

P.E.P.P.E.R., ALL ENERGY TO FRONT SHIELD AND MAIN REPULSOR RAYS. LET'S END THIS FAST.

DETECTING ENERGY FLUCTUATIONS FROM THE NORTH AND SOUTH QUADRANTS...

THEY'VE GOT SHIELDS.

YEP. THEY DO.

FABOOM

BAD NEWS. UNIDENTIFIED SPACECRAFT HAS ENTERED THE PERIMETER.

UH-OH! OH WAIT...

AGH!

STARK?

DVS-EFV-DFBGH-@$@#$SIRIUS HITS ONE!

GROOT!

GUARDIANS!

BACK TO THE SHIP NOW!

#1 & **#2 VARIANTS** BY JOE QUESADA, DANNY MIKI & RICHARD ISANOVE

"WHAT IS SO IMPORTANT ABOUT THE EARTH ALL OF A SUDDEN?"

...E NEGATIVE ZONE.
...K WEEKS AGO.

...FIRST THINGS ...FIRST, I WOULD ...KE TO WELCOME ...LL OF YOU, THE ...AL AMBASSADORS ...OF EACH OF THE GALACTIC EMPIRES...

I AM KING ...J-SON OF THE ...ROYAL CONCLAVE OF SPARTAX.

I INTRODUCE TO YOU THE **SUPREME INTELLIGENCE** OF THE KREE EMPIRE.

GLADIATOR, LEADER OF THE SHI'AR.

YOUNG ANNIHILUS, LEADER OF THE NEGATIVE ZONE AND OUR HOST.

QUEEN OF THE BROOD.

THE ALL-MOTHER OF THE ASGARDIANS, FREYJA.

Y-GAAAR OF THE BROTHERHOOD OF THE BADOON.

IT IS VERY ...OOD, AFTER ALL ...AT WE HAVE BEEN ...HROUGH, TO SEE YOU HERE.

I HOPE THAT THIS IS THE FIRST ...A LONG LINE OF SUCH ...EETINGS--WHERE WE ...N GATHER TO DISCUSS ...SSUES WHICH AFFECT US ALL.

AND, YES, WE GATHER HERE TODAY TO DISCUSS ONE PLANET WHOSE VERY EXISTENCE MAY BE A THREAT TO EACH OF OUR WELL-BEING.

IF NOT TODAY, CERTAINLY IN THE LONG TERM, ONE PLANET HAS TURNED ITSELF INTO A **CAULDRON** OF IRRESPONSIBILITY.

A PLANET OF **MADNESS.**

DO YOU KNOW THAT A *WATCHER*...

...A BEING WHOSE SOLE PURPOSE IS TO WITNESS THE MOST SHOCKING, HORRIFYING MOMENTS IN THE GALAXY...

...HAS VISITED THE PLANET EARTH MORE TIMES THAN ANY OTHER PLANET IN THE GALAXY?

DO YOU KNOW THAT THE PLANET EATER GALACTUS HAS REPEATEDLY BEEN REBUFFED BY EARTHLINGS?

EARTHLINGS!

NUMEROUS TIMES!

THE ONLY RECORDED INCIDENT OF THIS EVER TAKING PLACE IN OUR ENTIRE GALAXY.

THE COSMIC FORCE KNOWN AS THE PHOENIX, A FORCE THAT HAS *DEVASTATED* AND DESTROYED COUNTLESS PLANETS IN OUR AND OTHER SYSTEMS...

BUT IT COMES TO EARTH...AND IT *CEASES TO EXIST*.

THE PIRATE THANOS HAS ATTEMPTED ON OCCASION TO TAKE THE EARTH FOR HIMSELF.

FOR HE BELIEVES THAT IT IS A CENTERPIECE, A CROSSROADS OF POWER, FOR THIS ENTIRE GALAXY.

IT IS BELIEVE BY LORD THAN THAT THE INFIN STONES ARE EARTH.

YES. OUR INTELLIGENCE BELIEVES THAT AS WELL.

IF THE EARTH IS *SO POWERFUL* MAYBE THANOS HAS THE RIGHT IDEA.

MAYBE IT NEEDS TO BE DOMINATED BY A SUPERIOR RACE *NOW*.

STRADDLED INTO SUBMISSION *NOW*.

BUT, MY POINT IS, GLADIATOR, I DON'T THINK THAT CAN BE DONE.

WHAT EXACTLY *ARE* YOU SAYING, J-SON?

LONDON, ENGLAND.

GUYS, FAST AND FURIOUS AND STAY IN CONTACT.

I HAVE THE SHOT.

IF YOU DON'T THINK YOU HAVE THE SHOT, DON'T TAKE IT.

SYNCHRONIZED ATTACK ON TARGET.

STAY WITH THE OTHER SHIPS. WE OUTNUMBER THEM.

BY YOUR COMMAND.

BUT THE GUARDIANS?

THE STARLORD IS BUT ONE SHIP. MOTHER COMMAND WILL TAKE CARE OF THEM.

AGH!

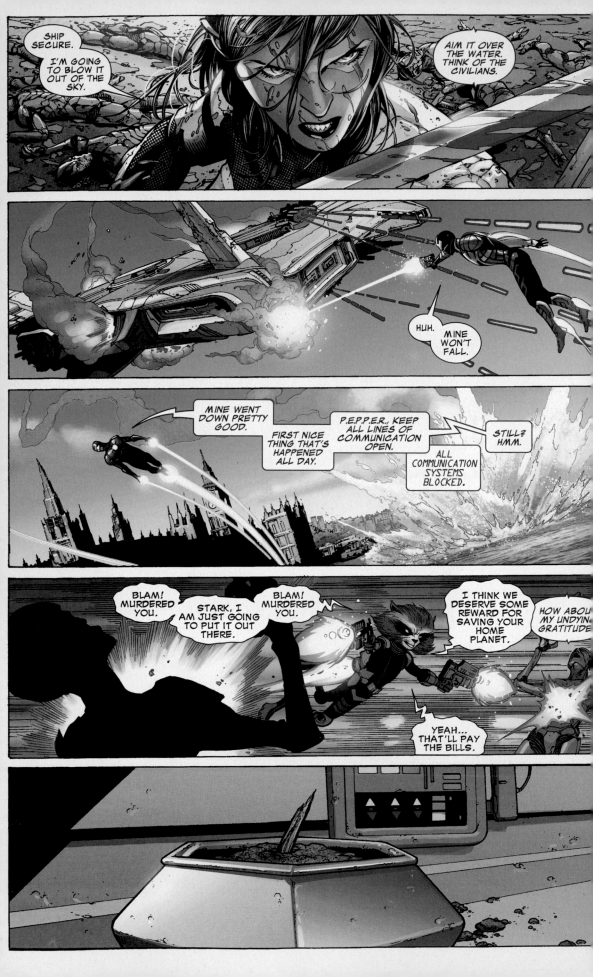

OKAY, LADIES OR WHATEVER YOU ARE UNDER THERE, IT WAS FUN AND ALL BUT UNLESS SOMEONE'S IN A CONFESSING MOOD AND WILLING TO JUST *TELL ME* WHY YOU'RE HERE WHEN YOU'RE SUPPOSED TO BE JUST ABOUT *ANYWHERE* ELSE...

I WOULD RATHER DIE!

DONE.

BLAM! MURDERED YOU!

HEY THERE, SKIZZIE.

SHOW ME THE SHIP'S SELF-DESTRUCT SEQUENCE.

NEVER! I WILL *NEVER*!

YEAH, OKAY.

BLAM! MURDERED YOU!

OH, I GOT THIS. I KNOW THIS SEQUENCE.

SHIP OVERRIDE.

SELF-DESTRUCT SEQUENCE ENGAGED.

HEY, DRAX, YOU ABOUT DONE OVER THERE?? HAVE AN IDEA.

ALMOST DONE!!

GET OFF YOUR SHIP.

IT'S ABOUT TO NOT BE THERE ANYMORE.

DARRGHH!

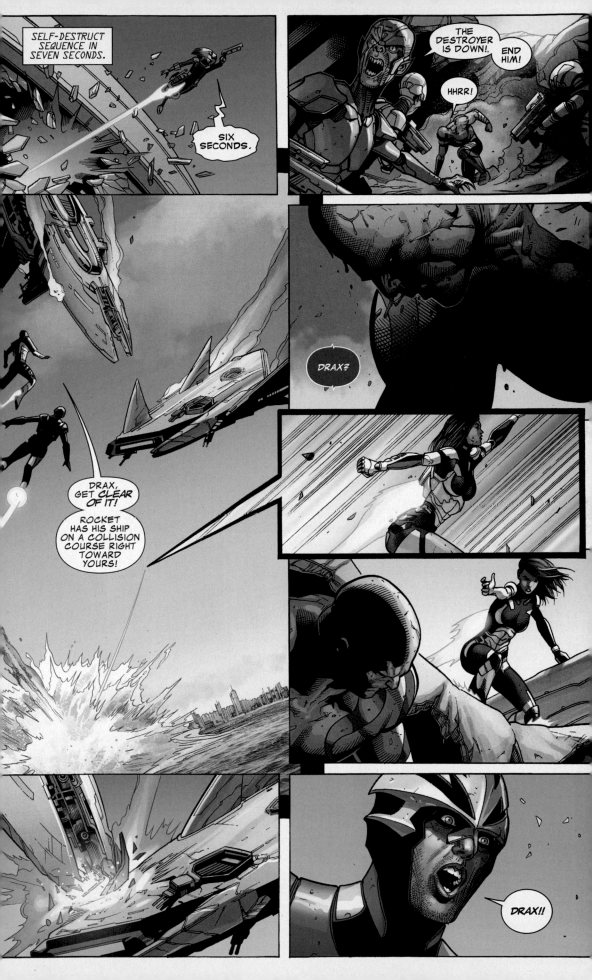

DO WE UNDERSTAND EACH OTHER OR IS A TRANSLATOR NEEDED?

WELL, THEN THAT'S ALL YOU HAD TO SAY.

I KNOW YOUR KIND, KING.

ALL TOO WELL.

EVERYONE OKAY?

I THINK THE BIG GUY IS HURT.

I'M FINE!!

YOU'RE NOT FINE.

LET GAMORA GET YOU BACK TO THE SHIP AND WE'LL--

I'M FINE!

DRAX, IT'S OKAY. WE CAN--

THAT'S NOT LIKE HIM.

HE'S DRAX THE DESTROYER.

WHAT'S HE USUALLY LIKE?

HEY, IT'S HIGHLY DISTURBING TO ME THAT COMMUNICATIONS ARE STILL BLOCKED.

STILL? DID WE GET ALL THE BADOON SHIPS?

ARE THERE MORE COMING?

SOMETHING IS STILL BLOCKING US.

DROP YOUR WEAPONS!!

#1 VARIANT BY SKOTTIE YOUNG

#2 VARIANT BY JOE MADU
& PETER STEIGERWALD

#3 VARIANT BY ED McGUINNESS, DEXTER VINES
& EDGAR DELGADO

#3 VARIANT BY LEINIL YU & SUNNY GHO

3

PLANET SPARTAX.
SHINING JEWEL OF THE SPARTAX EMPIRE.

MY KING.

I HAVE CLEAR WORD FROM THE ROYAL GUARD'S EARTH PLANET INITIATIVE.

THEY ARE *ALL* ALIVE AND IN CUSTODY. THEY ARE HEADED HERE.

AND THE BADOON TERRORISTS?

NO, SIR.

MY SON AND HIS BAND OF PIRATES TOOK OUT AN *ENTIRE FLEET* OF BADOON WARSHIPS?

ALL BY *THEMSELVES?*

THERE IS AN EARTHMAN AMONG THEM.

ARMORED.

AAAGGH! COME ON, GUYS! ARMOR DOESN'T GROW ON TREES, YOU KNOW!

WE DISMANTLED YOUR TRAPS AND NEGATED YOUR ENERGY SOURCE, EARTHER.

DO YOU HAVE ANYTHING ELSE TO DECLARE?

ROLLER SKATES.

PREPARE HIS STASIS TUBE.

IT'S READY.

HOW MUCH ARE YOU BEING PAID? BECAUSE I CAN ALMOST GUARANTEE--

BE QUIET, EARTHER.

I'M PRETTY SURE I CAN SET YOU UP WITH SPIDER-WOMAN--

SILENCE.

UH, LET'S TRY A DIFFERENT TACTIC. HOW ABOUT: YOU'RE ALL UNDER ARREST.

NO? NOTHING?

BE STILL. THIS IS PAINLESS.

I HAVE A QUESTION: HOW CAN WE UNDERSTAND EACH OTHER PERFECTLY?

WHAT ARE THE ODDS YOUR SPECIES SPEAKS THE SAME COLLOQUIAL ENGLISH THAT I--?

EVERY SHIP IN THE FLEET'S ATMOSPHERE IS EMBEDDED WITH A UNIVERSAL TRANSLATOR.

YOU DON'T HAVE THAT WHERE YOU'RE FROM?

OH MY GOD! THAT IS SO...

CCCCCCOOOLL...

THEY DON'T HAVE UNIVERSAL TRANSLATORS? HOW DO THEY GET ON?

I TOLD YOU, THEY'RE LIKE GLAVNARS.

HA!

THEY REALLY ARE.

THESE ARE TRICT ORDERS FROM THE CAPITAL CITY.

WE DO THIS BY PROCEDURE.

THIS BELONGS TO THE FEMALE, THANOS' DAUGHTER. I SAW IT IN HER ACTUALITY.

I WONDER IF THANOS KNOWS WHERE SHE IS.

YOU WONDER IF HE WILL COME LOOKING FOR HER.

YES.

THAT IS ENTIRELY WHAT I MEAN.

SHE IS A PRISONER OF WAR NOW.

I DON'T THINK THANOS WILL TAKE KINDLY TO THE NEWS.

ALL THE MORE REASON TO HURRY THIS UP.

WHO KNOWS WHAT MADNESS IS WAITING FOR US...

ACTING LIKE A PETULANT CHILD.

AND FOR THAT, GLADIATOR, HE AND HIS GUARDIANS ARE NOW OUR PRISONERS OF WAR.

YOU HAVE THEM?

HE WANTED TO MAKE AN EXAMPLE OF ME BUT I'M MAKING AN EXAMPLE OF HIM.

AND THAT'S HOW YOU RULE THE PEOPLE!!

I DON'T THINK IT CAN BE DONE.

IT WILL.

IS ANYONE ELSE GETTING TIRED OF HIM TALKING AS IF HE IS KING OF *US* AS WELL?

QUITE.

HE DOES NOT HAVE THE GUARDIANS.

IT IS NOT IMPOSSIBLE.

I WILL NOT BE SPOKEN TO IN SUCH A FASHION.

MY PEOPLE HAVE GONE TO *BLOOD WAR* FOR FAR LESS.

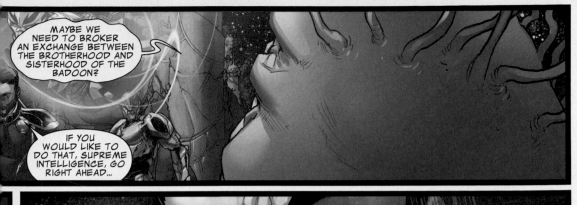

MAYBE WE NEED TO BROKER AN EXCHANGE BETWEEN THE BROTHERHOOD AND SISTERHOOD OF THE BADOON?

IF YOU WOULD LIKE TO DO THAT, SUPREME INTELLIGENCE, GO RIGHT AHEAD...

I WILL TAKE THAT AS A PROMISE.

AND THE NEXT TIME WE MEET, THAT PROMISE WILL BE KEPT.

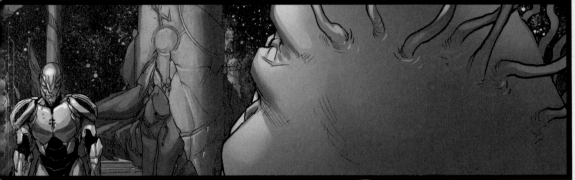

OVE SELF, AAR.

AND E J-SON ONG...

...AND YOU WILL HAVE ALL OUR RESPECT.

I BELIEVE KING J-SON IS PLAYING A MORE COMPLICATED GAME THAN WE FIRST REALIZED.

I AM ALMOST CERTAIN OF IT.

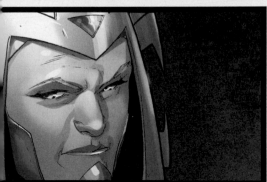

I AM...
.. GROOT.

YES, YOU ARE.

COMMAND CENTER BREACH!

PIUU PIUU PIUU PIUU

SECURED!

PIUU PIUU

OUR TURN!

HOW CAN YOU DO THIS TO US? WE ARE YOUR PEOPLE!

YOU ARE OUR PRINCE!

YOU STARTED IT.

LOVE SPARTAX TECH. CAN I KEEP IT?

CAN YOU SEE THE EARTH? IS IT IN ONE PIECE?

YEAH IT'S STILL THERE.

NO ALIEN SHIPS IN THE AREA.

ARE YOU SURE?

NOTHING ON ANY OF THEIR BROADCAST SIGNALS.

HEY, ROCKET, DO THAT THING WHERE EVERY SHIP IN THE SPARTAX FLEET CAN GET OUR SIGNAL WHETHER THEY LIKE IT OR NOT.

OH, I CAN DO THAT.

AAAAAND... ACTION.

OH, HELLO! GOOD MORNING, EVERYBODY.

THIS IS YOUR PRINCE STAR-LORD BROADCASTING LIVE FROM A SPARTAX WARSHIP THAT I JUST TOOK BY SHEER FORCE.

YOU SEE YOUR KING, MY FATHER, TRIED TO ARREST ME AND MY FRIENDS FOR STOPPING A HOSTILE AND UNPROVOKED INVASION OF EARTH BY AN ENEMY SPECIES.

YOU REALLY DO HAVE TO ASK YOURSELF WHY YOUR KING, AND MY FATHER, WOULD THINK IT NECESSARY TO ARREST SOMEONE FOR PROTECTING PEOPLE WHO CAN'T PROTECT THEMSELVES.

ASK YOURSELF: IF HE'S WILLING TO ARREST ME, HIS OWN FLESH AND BLOOD, FOR DOING THE RIGHT THING...

WHAT EXACTLY WOULD HE DO TO YOU GRUNTS IF YOU DID ANYTHING TO STAND IN HIS WAY?

SO CHEW ON THAT PUPPY, MY FELLOW SPARTAX WARRIORS.

THINK ABOUT THAT WHEN YOU TAKE YOUR NEXT ORDER.

THINK ABOUT THE MAN WHO'S GIVING THEM.

THINK ABOUT WHAT'S IN IT FOR YOU. IF ANYTHING.

GUARDIANS OF THE GALAXY: TOMORROW'S AVENGERS #1

NNN!

DO YOU FEEL THAT, DESTROYER?

I AM RIGELLIAN. I AM INSIDE YOUR HEAD. I FORCE YOUR SURRENDER.

THE RRRRRIGELLIAN THRUST.

ES! THE GELLIAN RUST OF HE MIND. YES.

YOU BATTLE ON ONLY THE PHYSICAL PLANE.

YOU ARE A BRUTE.

RIGELLIAN WAR IS OF MIND *AND* SOUL.

NUUGGH!

WHAT WILL BE THE FAMOUS GUARDIAN'S LAST SPOKEN WORD? WILL YOU BEG? WILL YOU HONOR ME?

NNYYAARGGHH!

BOOM

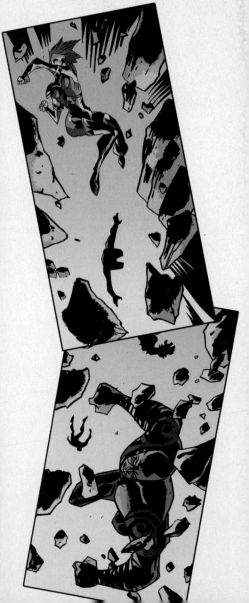

WILL THAT BE *YOUR* LAST SPOKEN WORD?

WHY DO YOU NOT FALL?

WHY DOES YOUR MIND NOT BUCKLE UNDER MY--?!

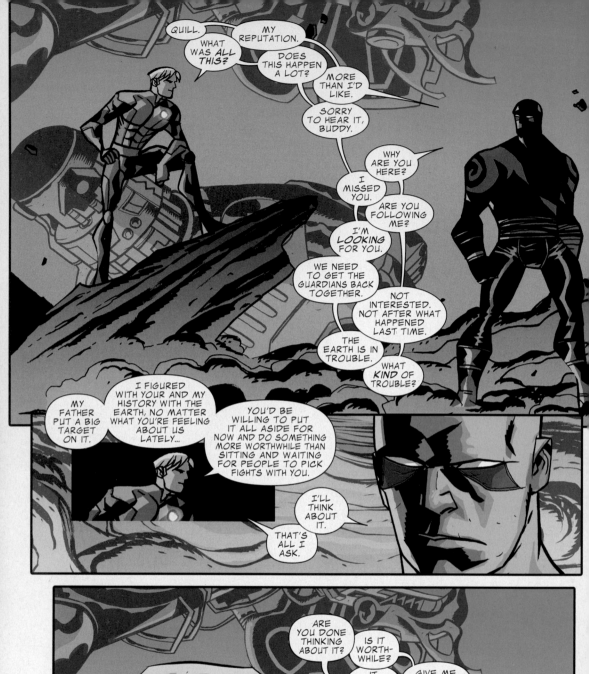

QUILL.

WHAT WAS *ALL* THIS?

MY REPUTATION.

DOES THIS HAPPEN A LOT?

MORE THAN I'D LIKE.

SORRY TO HEAR IT, BUDDY.

WHY ARE YOU HERE?

I MISSED YOU.

ARE YOU FOLLOWING ME?

I'M *LOOKING* FOR YOU.

WE NEED TO GET THE GUARDIANS BACK TOGETHER.

NOT INTERESTED. NOT AFTER WHAT HAPPENED LAST TIME.

THE EARTH IS IN TROUBLE.

WHAT *KIND* OF TROUBLE?

MY FATHER PUT A BIG TARGET ON IT.

I FIGURED WITH YOUR AND MY HISTORY WITH THE EARTH, NO MATTER WHAT YOU'RE FEELING ABOUT US LATELY...

YOU'D BE WILLING TO PUT IT ALL ASIDE FOR NOW AND DO SOMETHING MORE WORTHWHILE THAN SITTING AND WAITING FOR PEOPLE TO PICK FIGHTS WITH YOU.

I'LL THINK ABOUT IT.

THAT'S ALL I ASK.

ARE YOU DONE THINKING ABOUT IT?

IS IT WORTHWHILE?

IT IS TO US. AND THE EARTH.

GIVE ME SOMETHING WORTHWHILE TO DO, QUILL.

JUST PROMISE ME IT'LL BE WORTHWHILE.

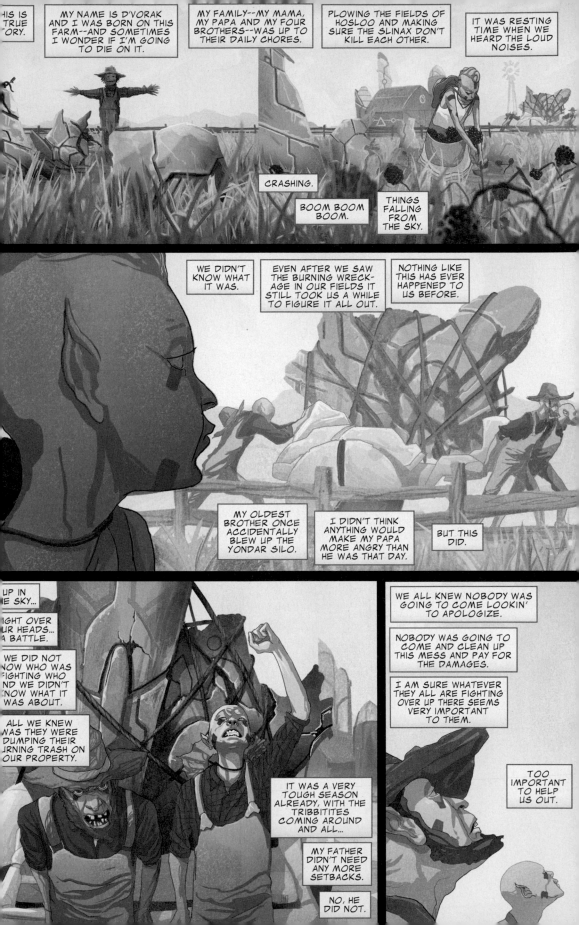

THAT JUST SEEMS INSANE TO ME.

WHY WOULD ANYBODY WANT TO LIVE THAT WAY?

THERE ARE PEOPLE IN MY SCHOOL, LIKE THAT RIDICULOUS CRISISO, THAT PRAY AND DREAM OF GETTING UP INTO THE STARS, FIGHTING SKRULLS AND KREE AND THE FIREBIRD OF PHOENIX.

I DON'T WANT TO LIVE ON THIS FARM BUT I KNOW I DON'T WANT TO LIVE UP--

TERRAN.

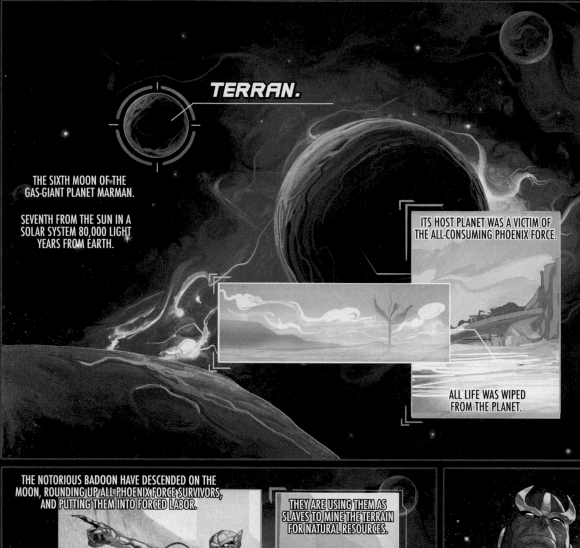

THE SIXTH MOON OF THE GAS-GIANT PLANET MARMAN.

SEVENTH FROM THE SUN IN A SOLAR SYSTEM 80,000 LIGHT YEARS FROM EARTH.

ITS HOST PLANET WAS A VICTIM OF THE ALL-CONSUMING PHOENIX FORCE.

ALL LIFE WAS WIPED FROM THE PLANET.

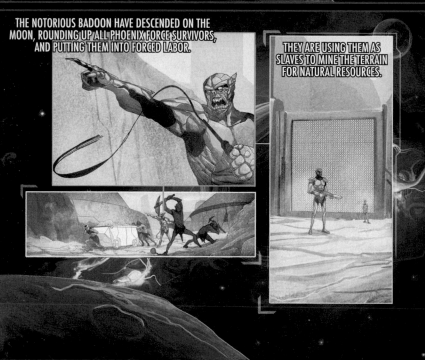

THE NOTORIOUS BADOON HAVE DESCENDED ON THE MOON, ROUNDING UP ALL PHOENIX FORCE SURVIVORS, AND PUTTING THEM INTO FORCED LABOR.

THEY ARE USING THEM AS SLAVES TO MINE THE TERRAIN FOR NATURAL RESOURCES.

ALL FOR THE GLORY OF THE MAD TITAN THANOS.

BUT THANOS HAS A DAUGHTER.

A WOMAN HE TRAINED TO BE THE MOST DANGEROUS WOMAN IN THE GALAXY.

BUT SHE HAS DECIDED HER FATHER IS A MONSTER AND NOW USES HER EVERY BREATH TO RUIN HIM.

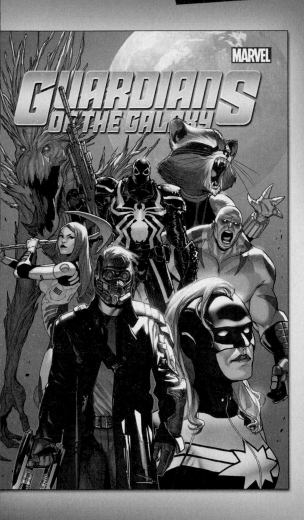

MARVEL AUGMENTED REALITY (AR) ENHANCES AND CHANGES THE WAY YOU EXPERIENCE COMICS!

TO ACCESS THE FREE MARVEL AR CONTENT IN THIS BOOK*:

1. Locate the **AR** logo within the comic.
2. Go to Marvel.com/AR in your web browser.
3. Search by series title to find the corresponding AR.
4. Enjoy Marvel AR!

*All AR content that appears in this book has been archived and will be available only at Marvel.com/AR — no longer in the Marvel AR App. Content subject to change and availability.

GUARDIANS OF THE GALAXY

AR INDEX

TO REDEEM YOUR CODE FOR A FREE DIGITAL COPY:

1. GO TO MARVEL.COM/REDEEM. OFFER EXPIRES ON 6/25/16.
2. FOLLOW THE ON-SCREEN INSTRUCTIONS TO REDEEM YOUR DIGITAL COPY.
3. LAUNCH THE MARVEL COMICS APP TO READ YOUR COMIC NOW!
4. YOUR DIGITAL COPY WILL BE FOUND UNDER THE *MY COMICS* TAB.
5. READ & ENJOY!

FM2HT7I4QPL

YOUR FREE DIGITAL COPY WILL BE AVAILABLE

| MARVEL COMICS APP FOR APPLE® iOS DEVICES | MARVEL COMICS AP FOR ANDROID™ DEVIC |

EXCLUSIVE COMPLETE GRAPHIC NOVEL!

MARVEL

BONUS! EXTRA DIGITAL ISSUE OF AVENGERS FREE!

AVENGERS

BRIAN MICHAEL BENDIS · JOHN ROMITA JR.

Avengers
by Brian Michael Bendis Vol. 1
ISBN # 978-0-7851-9211-4

EXCLUSIVE COMPLETE GRAPHIC NOVEL!

BRUBAKER
EPTING
LARK
LEON

MARVEL

BONUS! EXTRA DIGITAL ISSUE OF CAPTAIN AMERICA FREE!

CAPTAIN AMERICA

WINTER SOLDIER

"This book is exciting, fresh and new." — COMICBOOKRESOUCES.COM

ALIENS, ROCKET LAUNCHERS AND SWORDS — OH MY!

The galaxy is in chaos. Warring empires and cosmic terrorists plague every corner. It's a good thing the Guardians of the Galaxy are around to fight for those who have no champions. Peter Quill is their indomitable leader, the Earth-born Star-Lord with a penchant for trouble. At his side fight the green-skinned Gamora, former criminal and present Deadliest Woman in the Universe; Drax the Destroyer, the man with the destruction; Rocket Raccoon, creature of big guns and sharp teeth; and the flowery — but formidable — Groot. Earth has been declared off-limits — but when the alien Badoon launch an invasion of London, it's to the Guardians to protect the planet!

ISBN 978-0-7851-9209-1

5050

9 780785 192091

$5.00 US

MARVEL.COM

MARVEL 75 YEARS

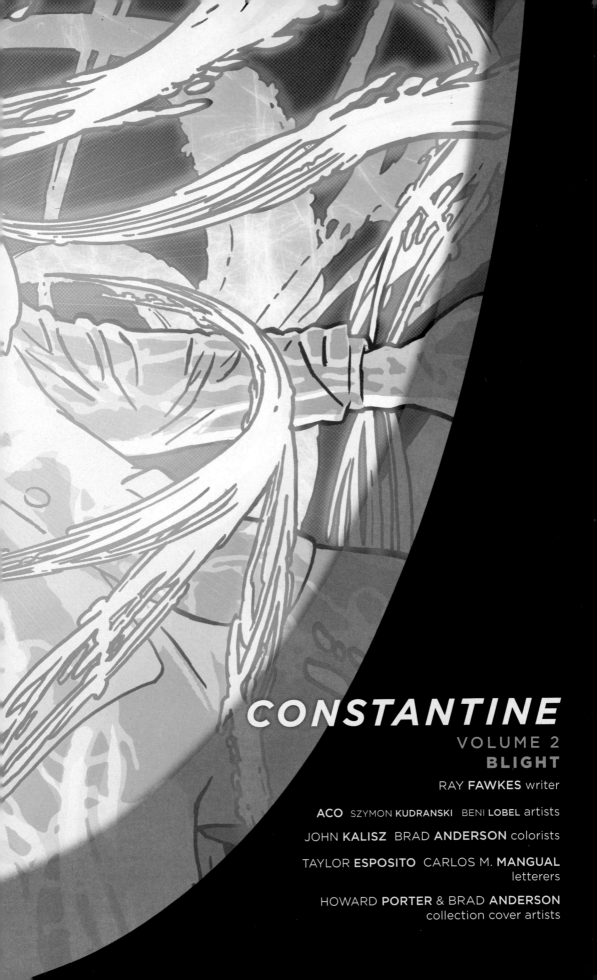

CONSTANTINE

VOLUME 2
BLIGHT

RAY **FAWKES** writer

ACO SZYMON **KUDRANSKI** BENI **LOBEL** artists

JOHN **KALISZ** BRAD **ANDERSON** colorists

TAYLOR **ESPOSITO** CARLOS M. **MANGUAL**
letterers

HOWARD **PORTER** & BRAD **ANDERSON**
collection cover artists

BRIAN CUNNINGHAM Editor – Original Series KATE DURRE Assistant Editor – Original Series ROWENA YOW Editor
ROBBIN BROSTERMAN Design Director – Books ROBBIE BIEDERMAN Publication Design

DIANE NELSON President DAN DIDIO and JIM LEE Co-Publishers
GEOFF JOHNS Chief Creative Officer
AMIT DESAI Senior VP – Marketing and Franchise Management
AMY GENKINS Senior VP – Business and Legal Affairs NAIRI GARDINER Senior VP – Finance
JEFF BOISON VP – Publishing Planning MARK CHIARELLO VP – Art Direction and Design
JOHN CUNNINGHAM VP – Marketing TERRI CUNNINGHAM VP – Editorial Administration
LARRY GANEM VP – Talent Relations and Services
ALISON GILL Senior VP – Manufacturing and Operations HANK KANALZ Senior VP – Vertigo and Integrated Publishing
JAY KOGAN VP – Business and Legal Affairs, Publishing JACK MAHAN VP – Business Affairs, Talent
NICK NAPOLITANO VP – Manufacturing Administration SUE POHJA VP – Book Sales
FRED RUIZ VP – Manufacturing Operations COURTNEY SIMMONS Senior VP – Publicity BOB WAYNE Senior VP – Sales

CONSTANTINE VOLUME 2: BLIGHT

DC Comics, 1700 Broadway, New York, NY 10019
A Warner Bros. Entertainment Company.
Printed by RR Donnelley, Salem, VA, USA. 11/26/14. Second Printing.
ISBN 978-1-4012-4747-8

Library of Congress Cataloging-in-Publication Data

Fawkes, Ray, author.
Constantine. Volume 2 / Ray Fawkes, Renato Guedes.
pages cm. — (The New 52!)
ISBN 978-1-4012-4747-8 (paperback)
1. Graphic novels. I. Guedes, Renato, illustrator. II. Title.
PN6727.C675F39 2014
741.5'973—dc23

2014011701

SUSTAINABLE
FORESTRY
INITIATIVE

Certified Chain of Custody
20% Certified Forest Content,
80% Certified Sourcing
www.sfiprogram.org
SFI-01042
APPLIES TO TEXT STOCK ONLY

A **CHILL** HAS SETTLED ON THE CITY THIS OCTOBER MORNING, A RIME OF EARLY FROST JUST KISSING THE PAVEMENT.

NO!

JOHN CONSTANTINE TAKES RAGGED, SCRAPING, GASPING BREATHS, **PAINFUL** BREATHS, BUT HE CAN'T STOP RUNNING.

NO!

HE STARTED THE MOMENT HE REALIZED HE WAS **NO LONGER DEAD,** BECAUSE HE KNOWS THAT KILLING HIM WAS NOT THE **WORST** THING HIS ENEMIES COULD DO.

NO!

YOU BASTARD--

NONONO--

AND AS HE RACES THROUGH THE SHATTERED CAGES OF **DOTTY'S PET SHOP,** HE TRIES TO IGNORE EVERY INDICATION THAT HE IS **TOO LATE...**

PLEASE...

...THOUGH HE KNOWS THAT THEY WILL HAVE LEFT **NOTHING** TO CHANCE, HE HAS TO **HOPE.** AND IF HE'S GOING TO HOLD ON TO THAT HOPE, HE HAS TO **RUN,** RUN WITH EVERY LAST OUNCE OF STRENGTH...

...UNTIL HE'S GOT NOTHING LEFT.
BLOODY HELL! EVERYTHING. THEY TOOK EVERY-THING!
I'VE LOST!

WHAT'S HAPPENING?

C'MON, JOHN, HOLD IT TOGETH--

HRAUGGH!

DOTTY.

DOTTY, CAN YOU HEAR ME?

AH. JOHN? I DIDN'T SEE YOU COME IN.

OH, JOHN. A MAN WAS HERE. A MAGICIAN, LIKE YOU.

HE SHOWED ME THAT MY GEORGE IS IN HEAVEN. HE HELPED ME SPEAK WITH HIM.

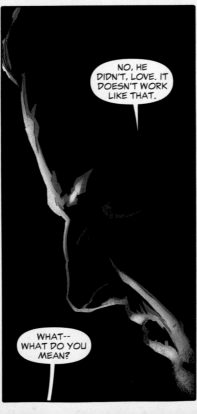

NO, HE DIDN'T, LOVE. IT DOESN'T WORK LIKE THAT.

WHAT-- WHAT DO YOU MEAN?

LOOK INTO MY EYES, YEAH?

HE PUT A SPELL IN YOUR MIND, AND I NEED TO MAKE SURE IT--

I NEED TO MAKE SURE YOU'RE ALL RIGHT.

"YOU POOR SOUL."

SAVONA, ITALY.

YOUR EYES...YOU MUST HAVE SUFFERED TERRIBLY. WERE YOU...A SOLDIER?

SO COMPASSIONATE. BUT LET'S NOT GET OFF THE SUBJECT AT *HAND*, SHALL WE?

AH'VE MADE MYSELF AT *HOME* WHILE YOU WERE OUT, SIGNOR. AH'VE DISCERNED SOME *VERY* INTERESTING THINGS ABOUT YOUR MYSTIC TALENTS WHILE AH WAITED FOR YOU TO RETURN.

WHO *ARE* YOU? WHAT ARE YOU *DOING* HERE?

THEY CALL YOU *IL STREGONE*. AH KNOW YOU'VE BEEN HIDDEN HERE FOR SOME TIME, AND AH KNOW YOU'VE YET TO BE APPROACHED BY THE *COLD FLAME*.

BUT FOR ALL YOUR GENTLE YEARS OF *ENCHANTMENT*, ALL YOUR HEALING AND YOUR HEROISM, THERE IS A *PRICE* TO PAY.

HMM. EVERY SO OFTEN, SOMEBODY SHOWS UP ON MY DOORSTEP LIKE YOU, AND TELLS ME I MUST *PAY* THEM, YES?

THEY ASSUME THAT I AM WEALTHY, FROM MY DEEDS. AND I SAY NOW WHAT I ALWAYS SAY:

YOU GET NOTHING FROM ME. I ONLY PAY IN THE *NEXT* WORLD.

YOU MIS-UNDERSTAND ME, SIGNOR.

I'M HERE TO MAKE *THAT* HAPPEN.

FOR **TANNARAK**, THIS IS THE MOMENT OF **TRUTH**. HE PAUSES TO LOOK BACK AT THE TEMPLE HE **BUILT**, WITH HIS ALLIES ALL THOSE YEARS AGO.

THE MANY **VENERATED** ARTIFACTS HE STOLE FROM CONSTANTINE'S VAULT LIE AT HIS FEET, THEIR **RICH** AND **VARIED** HISTORY IRRELEVANT NOW, INCONSEQUENTIAL.

HE DOESN'T CARE ABOUT OLD **STORIES**. HE HAS NO TIME FOR **MYTHS**.

FCOOOSH

THE ONLY VALUE THEY REPRESENT ...

TERREBONNE PARISH, LOUISIANA.

FELIX FAUST feels the thrum of purloined magic BURN his hand as it cracks over the hemisphere like a WHIP.

He curses to himself to cover his sudden, inexplicable TERROR.

TWENTY MILES ABOVE ICELAND.

In the silence of the stratosphere, THE SPECTRE turns away from the moon to watch the wave of power swing suddenly to the north American COAST.

A fundamental DISTORTION follows in its wake, and the spirit of DIVINE VENGEANCE wonders if his attentions will soon be required.

CITY OF DIS, INFERNO.

Perched on the side of the Tower of Thorns, ETRIGAN THE DEMON senses a bristling in the fabric of the world's UNDERSIDE. The great ribbon of magic breaches the skies of HELL like a beast cresting a wave, then disappears again.

He laughs, for it is a PERVERSION, and he finds that DELIGHTFUL.

NEW YORK CITY.

And PAPA MIDNITE cradles the headless body of his agent, and his only chance to find and retrieve the boy's SOUL is disrupted by the SHRIEK of unimaginable energies passing over.

CONSTANTINE, YOU FOOL...

WE ARE-- I AM FAR, FAR MORE POWERFUL THAN YOU KNOW NOW.

MY FATHER POSSESSED THE FAMED RUBY OF LIFE, AND IT GAVE HIM DOMINION OVER THE ELEMENTS. I AM THE RUBY NOW, AND MUCH MORE. THE VERY FABRIC OF THE WORLD IS MINE TO COMMAND.

I USED TO DREAM OF KILLING YOU WHEN I WAS AN APPRENTICE. DID YOU KNOW THAT? AT LEAST ONE NIGHT A WEEK, I AWOKE FROM THE IMAGE OF MY HAND CLASPED AROUND YOUR THROAT.

I ASKED MY FATHER WHAT IT MEANT.

CHEEKY SOD-- HNNGH...

...PROBABLY SAID IT MEANT YOU WERE A GENTLE PRINCESS.

HE SAID--ARE YOU LISTENING?

WHEN THE TIME COMES, HE SAID, IT MEANT THAT YOUR FATE WOULD BE MINE TO DECIDE.

OLD SARGON WAS NEVER GREAT AT--NNGH...

...DREAM INTERPRETATION, Y'KNOW. BUT HE WAS A HELL OF A GOOD MASSEUR.

LONDON, ENGLAND.

WAIT A MINUTE.

STOP! I KNOW WHO YOU ARE!

HNNNGH...

DO YOU NOW?

MAMA?

AH FOUND THIS PHOTO HIDDEN AMONG YOUR *UNMENTIONABLES*.

AH KNOW YOU WERE CONSTANTINE'S LOVER ONCE. DOES YOUR HUSBAND KNOW YOU STILL CARRY A *TORCH*?

I'VE NO MIND TO BE *KILLED*, NOR TO LOSE ME FAMILY. I KNOW HOW THIS *WORKS*.

M'NAME IS *JULIA EVERHEART* AND I'M A BLOODY *WITCH* AND NONE OF YOU HAVE EVER ASKED ME BEFORE AND I DO WANT TO *JOIN* THE COLD FLAME!

D'YOU HEAR ME?

AH HEAR YOU.

RULES ARE *RULES*. SEND YOUR DAUGHTER UPSTAIRS, MRS. EVERHEART, AND THEN TAKE MY *HAND*.

C'MON, YOU **KNOW** THE FEELING...

...GET THIS *ITCH* IN THE BACK OF YOUR HEAD, SAYS MAYBE **BE CAREFUL.** SAYS MAYBE EVERYTHING IS NOT WHAT IT **SEEMS.** AND JUST WHEN YOU DO...

GUY ACROSS THE TABLE *INSULTS* YOU.

WHY D'YOU THINK HE **DOES** THAT?

BECAUSE HE WANTS YOU ANGRY.

YEAH. YOU GET ANGRY, YOU STOP THINKING.

SO *THAT* HAPPENS, ESPECIALLY JUST BEFORE A BIG MOVE, NOW YOU **KNOW** YOU'RE BEING **PLAYED.** YOU SPOT THE **HUSTLE.**

THEN THERE'S ONLY **ONE** THING YOU CAN DO.

KEEP YOUR HEAD. GO **WITH** THE PLAY, AND WAIT FOR AN OPENING.

AND THEN?

THEN YOU DO SOMETHING **UNEXPECTED.**

RIGHT, JOHN...

"...SPOT THE HUSTLE."

HUH. VERY **GOOD.**

YOU'RE MORE **DISCIPLINED** THAN AH THOUGHT, CONSTANTINE. IT'S NOT AN EASY THING, TO LEAP OUT OF YOUR BODY LIKE THAT. WITH NO PREPARATION **WHATSOEVER.**

THE MORE AH DEAL WITH YOU, THE MORE AH **RESPECT** YOU.

AND THE MORE AH SEE HOW IMPORTANT IT IS TO **KILL** YOU.

YAP YAP

AH SEE YOUR **FEAR,** CONSTANTINE, AND YOUR **DOUBT** YOU **KNOW** YOU CAN'T WIN.

IF WE'RE GOING TO TALK, LET'S TALK.

IF WE'RE GOING TO FIGHT, LET'S **FIGHT.**

YAAGH!

HWHUH?

IS HE
DEAD?

NOT
YET.

RIGHT.

THAT'S JUST HOW I'D'VE PUT IT.

THE MOONBLADE I HOLD IS A UNIQUE WEAPON. IT CHANGES SHAPE WITH THE PHASES OF THE MOON, A LONG-SWORD WHEN IT'S FULL, AND A DAGGER WHEN IT'S NEW.

BUT IT REALLY PACKS A PUNCH OUTSIDE THE PHYSICAL. IT CAN HOLD CONCEPTS. THOUGHTS, DREAMS, AND STRANGE ENERGIES. THEY SAY IT ONCE HOUSED A GOD...

AND THAT IT CAN KILL JUST ABOUT ANYTHING.

"NOT YET."

YOUR RESPECT MEANS NOTHING TO ME, E.

YOU'RE A TWISTED WRECK, LONG PAST HIS PRIME. WITHOUT THIS LOT, YOU'D STILL BE RUNNING A FAITH-HEALING SCAM OUT OF YOUR CANVAS TENT IN MISSISSIPPI, YEAH?

HAH!

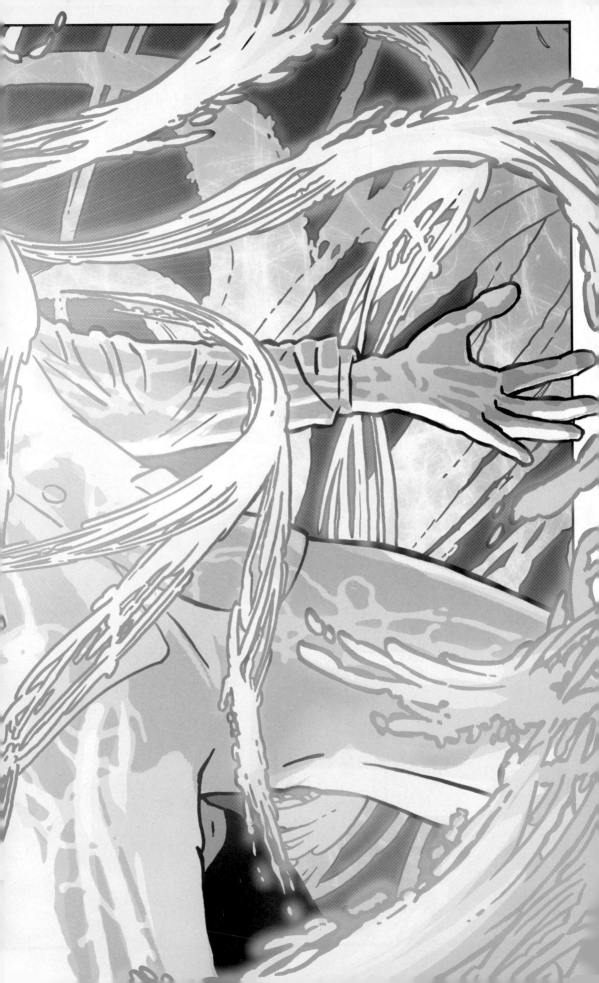

...SO THEY COULD CARVE HIM UP LIKE A BLOODY **PIE.**

OR **ME,** I SUPPOSE. IF THINGS WENT THE **OTHER** WAY.

AHHHHHH...

JOHN, YOU SWEET, SWEET MAN. AS INFURIATING AS YOU CAN BE--

--YOU **DO** KNOW JUST HOW TO MAKE A GIRL **HAPPY.**

IT MEANS THAT THEY WERE **PLANNING** FOR THIS. WAITING FOR **MISTER E** TO DIE...

AND THERE IT IS. THE MOMENT HIS HEART **STOPS.**

ALL OF THE MAGIC HE'S BEEN HOLDING **INSIDE** HIMSELF. HIS TWO SO-CALLED **ALLIES** GRAB IT ALL FOR THEMSELVES WITH THEIR DAMNED **RITUAL.** WHICH MEANS WHAT?

SARGON, THE BLOODY WOULD-BE GODDESS OF A **NEW AGE...**

...AND HIDDEN SOMEWHERE IN HIS LAIR, THE GREATEST MYSTIC GENIUS OF HIS TIME...

...TANNARAK.

...AND A COUPLE OF HOURS LATER, ONCE I'VE SWORN THEIR OATHS AND BOWED AT THEIR FEET AND SWALLOWED THEIR DRUGGED WINE, ONCE WE'RE ALL SMILES...

...I DO SOMETHING UNEXPECTED.

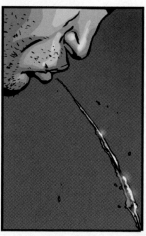

YOU SON OF A BITCH.

FEEL FREE TO SPEAK YOUR MIND, GUV. WE'RE ALONE HERE.

YOU *DISAPPOINT* ME, CONSTANTINE. A GREAT CHANCE TO SHOW YOUR *METTLE* AND YOU GO *HALFWAY*. RUNNING ME THROUGH WITH THIS *CHARLATAN'S TOY* AND TRAPPING MY SPIRIT WITHIN. FOR *WHAT?*

TO *BIND* ME TO SOME SORDID *SERVICE*, NO DOUBT. TO *HUMILIATE* ME, TO FORCE ME TO LISTEN TO MY OWN ALLIES *INSULT* ME.

YOU HAVE SUCH *TALENT*, CONSTANTINE, AND YOU *SQUANDER* IT BECAUSE YOU ARE *PETTY* AND *DEPRAVED*.

MAYBE SO...

...BUT YOU'RE RIGHT ABOUT ONE THING. YOUR SPIRIT IS STUCK IN THE SWORD AS LONG AS I *WANT* IT THERE. THAT'S WHAT A MOONBLADE'S FOR, YEAH? STORING *DREAMS* AND *THOUGHTS*. I FIGURED A LITTLE TWEAK AND I COULD HOLD ON TO *YOU*.

YOU SHOULD'VE *KILLED* ME. I'LL MAKE YOU *REGRET* THIS.

BUT *I* DIDN'T BRING THE SWORD HERE...

...MISTER E.

YOUR PEOPLE DID. TANNARAK TOOK IT OUT OF MY VAULT. *SARGON* LEFT IT ON THE BALCONY.

THEY SET YOU *UP*.

RIGHT NOW THEY'RE *LAUGHING*, FIZZING WITH THE POWER THEY TOOK FROM YOUR *CORPSE*. SO WHAT ARE YOU GOING TO *DO* ABOUT IT?

HHHAH...

...NOT A BAD *VIEW*, AT LEAST.

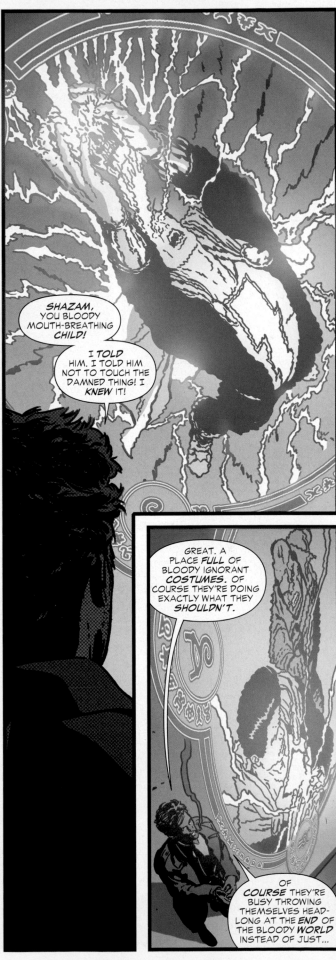

SHAZAM, YOU BLOODY MOUTH-BREATHING *CHILD!*

I *TOLD* HIM. I TOLD HIM NOT TO TOUCH THE DAMNED THING! I *KNEW* IT!

GREAT. A PLACE *FULL* OF BLOODY IGNORANT *COSTUMES.* OF COURSE THEY'RE DOING EXACTLY WHAT THEY *SHOULDN'T.*

OF *COURSE* THEY'RE BUSY THROWING THEMSELVES HEADLONG AT THE *END* OF THE BLOODY *WORLD* INSTEAD OF JUST...

NO.

LOOK AT THIS. EIGHT MILLION PEOPLE STUCK IN A CITY WITHOUT *HOPE*. NO POWER. NO HEAT. NO PHONES, NO RADIO.

ABOUT FIVE YEARS AGO, I STARTED SEEING THE *COSTUMES* MUCKING ABOUT IN THE WORLD. WAVING AND GRINNING, FLEXING *POWER* THEY CLEARLY DIDN'T UNDERSTAND.

DIDN'T TAKE ME MORE THAN TEN *MINUTES* TO GROW A HEALTHY DISTASTE FOR THEM AND THEIR BRAND OF MORAL IMPERATIVE, YEAH? "JUSTICE."

I DID WHAT A *LOT* OF PEOPLE DID.

I WISHED THEY'D JUST *GO AWAY*.

THEN MY *GIRLFRIEND* BECAME ONE OF THEM.

AND THEN, WELL...

...THEN I GOT WHAT I *WISHED* FOR, DIDN'T I?

ZATANNA ISN'T **DEAD**. SHE CAN'T BE.

SHE'S OUT THERE, **SOMEWHERE**, IN THIS WORLD GONE DARK.

CAN'T LOCATE HER, THOUGH. NOBODY CAN. IT'S LIKE BLIGHT IS GENERATING A CURTAIN OVER ALL THE MYSTIC PLANES, POWERED BY THE EVIL UNLEASHED IN THE **CRIME SYNDICATE'S** INVASION.

LAST I SAW HER, WE WERE REACHING FOR EACH OTHER. WE BOTH **KNEW** IT'D ALL GONE **PEAR-SHAPED** AND THERE WAS NO FIGHTING BACK. I COULD SEE IT IN HER EYES.

WHOOOM

I DON'T KNOW IF I WAS TRYING TO RESCUE **HER**, OR IF SHE WAS TRYING TO RESCUE **ME**.

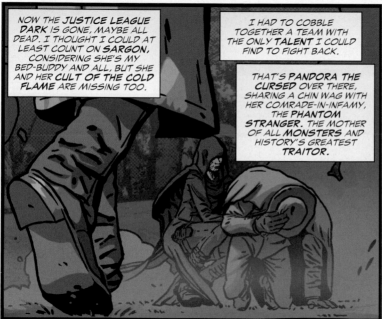

NOW THE **JUSTICE LEAGUE DARK** IS GONE, MAYBE ALL DEAD. I THOUGHT I COULD AT LEAST COUNT ON **SARGON**, CONSIDERING SHE'S MY BED-BUDDY AND ALL, BUT SHE AND HER **CULT OF THE COLD FLAME** ARE MISSING TOO.

I HAD TO COBBLE TOGETHER A TEAM WITH THE ONLY **TALENT** I COULD FIND TO FIGHT BACK.

THAT'S **PANDORA THE CURSED** OVER THERE, SHARING A CHIN WAG WITH HER COMRADE-IN-INFAMY, THE **PHANTOM STRANGER**. THE MOTHER OF ALL **MONSTERS** AND HISTORY'S GREATEST **TRAITOR**.

STILL, I'D RATHER SPEN[D] MY TIME WITH EITHER OF THEM THAN THE **NIGHTMARE NURSE**.

I DON'T SEE *YOU* HELPING, CONSTANTINE!

NO! STOP *SHOOTING!*

BLAMM BLAMM BLAMM

THERE'S A LIVING *BOY* IN THERE! CAN'T YOU SEE HIM? THE CREATURE IS *USING* HIM AS A HOST!

I *KNOW* HIM!

THIS IS *MADNESS.*

WE NEED TO REGROUP. GET A SECOND TO--

YEAH. LET'S *BOOK* IT!

HOLD ON--

FFFFT

THEY CAN'T HIDE FROM US, MY SIN CREATURES--

"--THEY CAN NEVER ESCAPE *EVIL*."

SOMEWHERE ELSE.

YOU DON'T UNDERSTAND, DO YOU, WHELP? YOU CAN'T *RUN*. YOU CAN'T *HIDE*.

THIS ISN'T A *GAME*. YOU ATTEMPTED TO ESCAPE *ONCE*.

YOU'LL WEAR THE SCARS OF *RETRIEVAL* FOR THE REST OF YOUR WORTHLESS LIFE.

YEAH, YEAH.

YOU'RE LUCKY I *NEED* SOMEONE WITH YOUR *TALENT* TO ASSIST ME IN RUNNING THIS *PROJECT* FOR THE CRIME SYNDICATE. OTHERWISE YOU'D BE UP THERE WITH THE *SUBJECTS*.

AND YOU DON'T WANT *THAT*.

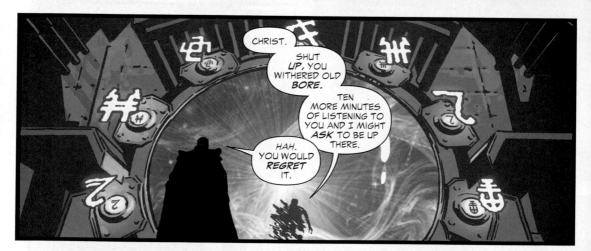

CHRIST.

SHUT *UP*, YOU WITHERED OLD *BORE*.

TEN MORE MINUTES OF LISTENING TO YOU AND I MIGHT *ASK* TO BE UP THERE.

HAH. YOU WOULD *REGRET* IT.

BUT YOU *WOULD* MAKE A SUITABLE SUBJECT.

SO DON'T *PUSH* ME.

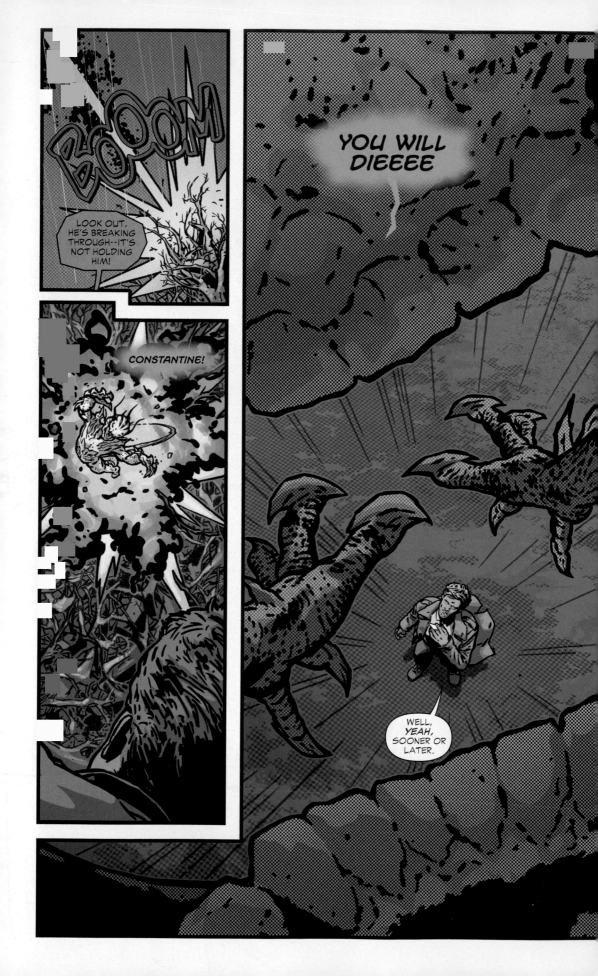

BUT THAT'S A LIE I'M TELLING MYSELF, ISN'T IT?

I ESCAPED WHEN THE CRIME SYNDICATE TOOK DOWN HER SUPERHERO FRIENDS. I CUT OUT AND LEFT HER BEHIND.

I'M SLEEPING WITH SARGON-- ONE OF HER SWORN FOES. I'VE THROWN IN WITH THE CULT OF THE COLD FLAME--THE ONES WHO VERY LIKELY KILLED HER FATHER.

ARGH!

THE SINS ARE BACK, PANDORA--

EVERY TIME I SEE HER LATELY, I PLAY THE COLD BASTARD TO SHOW HER THAT I DON'T NEED HER.

SO I KNOW HOW SHE'D REALLY ANSWER MY EXCUSES.

"PAR FOR THE COURSE, JOHN."

"PAR FOR THE COURSE."

WHERE-- WHERE IS EVERYONE--?

I LOOK UP JUST IN TIME TO SEE THE SWAMP THING GET SNAPPED IN HALF.

HE MAKES A SOUND EXACTLY LIKE BITING FRESH CELERY. I NEARLY LAUGH.

I CAN'T SEE ANY OF THE OTHERS.

I CAN'T THINK FOR THE PAIN. MY LEG'S ON FIRE. SOME KIND OF POISON.

A WHIP CRACKS.

OH. THERE'S THE NURSE.

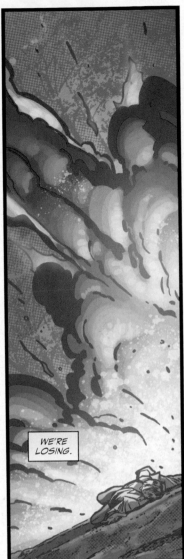

WE'RE LOSING.

ZEE, WE'RE LOSING THIS ONE. I LOVE YOU.

I'LL MAKE YOU A DEAL. I'LL SPARE YOU THE HEARTLESS TWIT ROUTINE. AND YOU...

...YOU TELL ME WE'LL FIGURE SOMETHING OUT.

IT'S ALL A **ONE-WAY** TRIP THESE DAYS, YEAH?

THINGS JUST GO FROM **BAD** TO **WORSE.**

WHILE THE WHOLE WORLD GOES TO HELL AT THE HANDS OF COSTUMED **MASS-MURDERERS,** SOME KIND OF BLANKET ENERGY IS MAKING IT IMPOSSIBLE TO FIND AND GATHER THE MYSTICS WHO MIGHT BE ABLE TO **DO SOMETHING** ABOUT IT.

MOST OF MY ALLIES...

...HELL, MOST OF MY **ENEMIES,** TOO-- ANYONE WORTH A **DAMN,** POWER-WISE, IS MISSING. IMPOSSIBLE TO FIND.

HONESTLY, THE ONLY ONE I NEED IS **ZATANNA.**

THE CREATURE **GENERATING** THAT ENERGY IS A MONSTROUS PATCHWORK OF HUMANITY'S EVIL, STITCHED TOGETHER IN THE **COLLECTIVE UNCONSCIOUS.** ITS NAME IS **BLIGHT.**

WE TRIED TO DISPELL IT ON ITS HOME PLANE, AND IT TOOK US TO **PIECES.** THEN IT FOLLOWED US INTO THE **REAL** WORLD AND TOOK POSSESSION OF A HUMAN **BOY.** NOW IT'S MAKING A BLOODY PLAYGROUND OF THE **EARTH** WHILE IT FEEDS ON THE EXTRA HELPINGS OF DARKNESS BROUGHT ON BY THE **COSTUMES.**

WE HAVE TO DEFEAT THIS THING OR WE'RE ALL **BUGGERED** EVERY WHICH WAY. 'COURSE SOMEONE STARTS TALKING ABOUT HOW WE NEED **GOD'S** HELP. ME, I HAPPEN TO REPLY THAT WHEN MY TIME COMES, I'D LOVE TO GIVE ANY GOD THAT LETS ALL **THIS** HAPPEN A PIECE OF MY **MIND...**

PANDORA FEELS THE PAIN OF EVIL MORE TRUTHFULLY THAN YOU CAN *EVER* KNOW. FOR TEN THOUSAND YEARS, SHE HAS SOUGHT TO *DESTROY* IT UTTERLY. CARVE IT OUT OF THE WORLD.

SHE IS [C]URSED FOR [B]RTHING EVIL [I]O THIS WORLD, [W]HICH SHE *DID NOT DO.*

[SH]E FIGHTS TO [DES]TROY EVIL, BUT [DOE]S SHE FIGHT ON [BEH]ALF OF THOSE [WH]O SUFFER ITS [ ]EFFECTS?

OR JUST TO END HER *OWN* PAIN?

WHO *CARES?!*

IF YOU'RE GOING TO REFUSE TO HELP, JUST TELL US YOU MOVE IN *MYSTERIOUS* BLOODY WAYS AND LEAVE US *BE!*

[ ]BOSTON [B]RAND, THE [DE]ADMAN," IS A [GOO]D MAN WITH A [GOO]D HEART. HE [IS]CHARITABLE, [HO]NEST, AND [ ]LOVING.

YOU BOUND HIM TO THE GENOCIDAL *SEA KING,* ONE OF YOUR MONSTERS FROM THE OTHER UNIVERSE.

WHEN THE WIND BLOWS ONE WAY, HE WILL BE *KIND.* WHEN IT *TURNS,* HE WILL UNLEASH *HORRORS.*

STOP THIS. STOP IT NOW. GIVE ME WHAT I NEED TO GET THE *JOB* DONE OR--

LOOK HERE...

...WE'RE **OUT.** I PULL HIM **WITH** ME.

AFTER THE WARMTH OF HEAVEN'S SHORE, THE HOUSE OF MYSTERY FEELS *ICE COLD.*

HOUSE! GIVE ME A **CELESTIAL CIRCLE!**

NO. WHAT--

WHAT IS THIS? I HAD **YOU!**

WHERE--?

ZAURIEL, MY FRIEND, YOU'VE BEEN **SNARED.** WELCOME TO THE MATERIAL WORLD.

STILL GOT ALL ME **PARTS,** TOO. NOT BAD.

CONSTANTINE! WHAT FOLLY IS THIS?

CLANG

YOUR SHAGGY FRIEND WASN'T **HELPING.** I THOUGHT I'D SNAG ONE OF HIS **LIEUTENANTS** TO HELP US OUT WITH BLIGHT.

THOUGHT I WAS GOING TO HAVE TO RESCUE YOU LOT, TOO.

YOU **STOLE** ME FROM THE **LIGHT?**

YO FOLLO ME, G

WHAT DO YOU *MEAN* HE WASN'T *HELPING?*

ALL HE DID WAS TELL ME WHY I COULDN'T TRUST *ANY* OF YOU.

WHAT? ARE YOU *KIDDING* ME?

HE SHOWED ME HOW THERE WAS STILL SOMETHING *GOOD* IN EACH OF US!

HE TOLD ME THAT MY HUMAN *SOUL* REMAINS.

AND THAT *YOU* SHINE WITH LOVE FOR--

PLEASE.

DON'T TELL ME ABOUT MY SHINING LOVE.

HE SHOWED ME THAT WE *DO* HAVE THE STRENGTH TO DEFEAT BLIGHT. THAT WE CAN ACCESS IT--

SO WE EACH HAD A DIFFERENT EXPERIENCE, DID WE?

I GET *TORMENTED* WHILE YOU ALL GET THE *PEP* TALK, YEAH?

TYPICAL.

NO, NOT *TYPICAL* AT ALL.

DON'T YOU SEE?

IF I HAD THREE BLOODY WISHES, THE FIRST ONE WOULD BE TO SEND NANDA PARBAT AND ITS LOVELY PICTURESQUE *MOUNTAINS* OFF INTO ORBIT SOMEWHERE.

BLOODY WELLSPRING OF MYSTIC ENERGY. AS IF THE WORLD *NEEDS* ONE OF THOSE. SHOULD'VE *KNOWN* WE'D END UP HERE. BUT *NO*, I SAID. USE YOUR *HEAD*, I SAID.

THAT WOULD BE TOO *OBVIOUS*.

SO THE MAD EXTRADIMENSIONAL COSTUMES CALLING THEMSELVES THE *CRIME SYNDICATE* ATTACK OUR WORLD. AND WHERE THE *JUSTICE LEAGUE* FALLS, I DO THE SKIN-OF-ME-TEETH ROUTINE.

AND THE *SYNDICATE* TIP THE WORLD'S PSYCHIC SCALES WELL INTO *EVIL'S* FAVOR, WHICH DRAWS TOGETHER A MONSTER IN HUMANITY'S *COLLECTIVE UNCONSCIOUS*. THE CREATURE CALLS ITSELF *BLIGHT*.

EYES OPEN, EVERYONE.

WE'RE IN, BUT WE STILL NEED TO BE *CAREFUL*.

AND I CAN'T FIND *ZATANNA* OR OST OF THE *JUSTICE LEAGUE* RK FOR ALL THE PSYCHIC NOISE GHT KICKS UP. ALL I'VE GOT IS DMAN, BOUND TO THE CORPSE THE SYNDICATE'S *SEA KING*.

SO I CREATE A *NEW* JUSTICE LEAGUE DARK AND WE PUT PAID TO *BLIGHT*.

AND THEN WE FIND OUT THAT THE *SYNDICATE* HAVE CAPTURED MOST OF THE WORLD'S MYSTICS AND ARE KEEPING THEM HERE FOR SOME SILLY DAMN REASON.

PICKING UP ANYTHING, NIGHTMARE NURSE?

WE DID IT, JOHNNY. I CAN SENSE ZATANNA'S THOUGHTS.

SHE'S HERE, ALIVE.

SHE'S IN SOME KIND OF... MACHINE. AND SHE'S NOT ALONE.

DEADMAN OPENED THE DOOR. IF HE'S SMART, HE'LL BUY US MAYBE TEN MINUTES BEFORE WHOEVER'S *RUNNING* THIS PLACE REALIZES THAT THEY'RE BEING INVADED.

BUT WE TAKE NOT THREE STEPS BEFORE THE OLD GUT DOES A LURCH AND I REALIZE...

TAK

GUH!

RELAX.

YOU WERE IN SHOCK. ONE HELL OF A *SPELL*, WHATEVER THAT WAS.

AND THEN YOU WERE PAYING THE PRICE OF *DUN-KON-WEN*, RELIVING THE DEATH WE FAKED.

"TWO OF CLUBS."

THAT'S WHAT NICK CALLED IT. THOSE TINY SPHERES OF ENERGY, THEY HIT YOU *TWICE*.

WHERE ARE THE OTHERS?

I HAVE NO IDEA. I JUST WOKE UP *MYSELF*.

SERIOUSLY, JOHNNY, JUST RELAX A MOMENT. I NEED TO FIX YOU UP.

DAMN. I KNEW I SHOULD'VE CAST *TAG* AND *TRACK* CHARMS ON ALL OF THEM WHEN I HAD THE CHANCE.

I DON'T KNOW WHAT SHOULD SURPRISE ME MORE...

THAT YOU CONSIDERED *SPYING* ON YOUR OWN TEAM?

OR THAT YOU DIDN'T ACTUALLY DO IT.

WHEN WE FIRST CAME IN.

YOU SAID YOU COULD SENSE ZATANNA'S THOUGHTS, YEAH?

CAN YOU *FIND* HER?

BUT OUR *TEAM!*

WE CAN'T LEAVE THEM!

OF COURSE WE CAN. IT'S EASY. YOU JUST TELL ME WHERE TO GO, AND WE *GO* THERE.

AND WE PRESS ON. THE NURSE CALLS OUT THE TURNS AND I DO THE **HEAVY LIFTING.**

THE DEFENSES CHANGE **TONE** QUICKLY. THERE'S ANOTHER MAGE HELPING NICK OUT HERE.

THESE SPELLS CARRY THE DISTINCT AROMA OF A POINTY-HATTED **TOSSER,** SO I'M GOING TO GUESS WE'RE DEALING WITH **FELIX FAUST.** THE KIND OF WIZARD WHO REFERS TO HIMSELF IN **THIRD** PERSON.

I'M COMING, ZATANNA. THEIR DEFENSES MEAN **NOTHING.**

THEY CAN CALL UP ALL THE C-GRADE SERVANT **DEMONS** THEY LIKE. I'M NOT **MESSING ABOUT.** NOT THIS TIME.

I BREAK THE **SHIMMERING BARRIER** OF KHEL-PHRA LIKE A KID RIPPING THROUGH GIFT-WRAP.

ARE YOU WATCHING, NICK? I KNOW YOU ARE.

YOU'RE THE ONE WHO **TAUGHT** ME TO EAT PR... LIKE FAUST **ALIVE.** I WON... WHY YOU'RE LETTING H... SET THE PACE HERE?

UNLESS YOU AREN'T THE ONE IN CHARGE.

THE **THREADS OF ACHERON.** YEAH, THIS IS FAUST'S WORK. OBSOLETE MAGIC CAST WITH A SHAKY HAND. MIGHT BRING DOWN A **NOVICE.**

BUT WHERE ARE **YOU,** NICK?

WHERE ARE **YOU?**

THEY'RE CLOSE, JOHN. THEY'RE...

...AND SARGON.

BUT WHERE'S *ZATANNA?*

YOU TELL ME.

HUH?

I MEAN, YOU CAN READ THEIR THOUGHTS, CAN'T YOU?

WITH YOUR HEALING MAGIC.

SURE, YEAH. RIGHT.

I SENSE THEIR SUFFERING... THEY'VE ALL ENDURED *TERRIBLE* MYSTIC SURGERY. THIS IS SOME KIND OF... *WEAPONS* PROGRAM?

THEY'VE GOT THESE MAGES FUSED UP AND LOADED LIKE...BOMBS IN THIS MACHINE. REUSABLE *NUKES.* IT'S ALL TO *KILL* SOMETHING... SOMETHING THAT EVEN THE CRIME SYNDICATE IS AFRAID OF.

SOMETHING THAT'S *FOLLOWING* THEM? I CAN *SEE* IT, IT'S... AW, IT'S *HUGE,* IT'S--I DON'T WANT TO *KNOW* SOME OF THIS.

OH, NO? TOO MUCH FOR YOUR *SWEET,* DELICATE *MIND?*

EXCUSE ME?

I *BROUGHT* YOU HERE. I FOUGHT *BLIGHT* AT YOUR SIDE, I--

YEAH, YEAH.

BUT YOU BROUGHT ME TO *SARGON,* DIDN'T YOU? WHY WOULD YOU DO THAT?

YOU WERE SUPPOSED TO SHOW ME *ZATANNA,* NOT THE BLOODY GORMLESS BRAT QUEEN OF THE *COLD FLAME.*

I DON'T *CARE* WHAT HAPPENS TO SARGON, YOU BLOODY FOOL.

I WANT *ZEE.*

JOHN, SARGON IS CONSCIOUS. SHE CAN *HEAR* YOU.

WH--

BAM

NO MORE GAMES. STOP IT, NOW.

I KNOW YOU AREN'T THE NURSE.

STOP THIS!

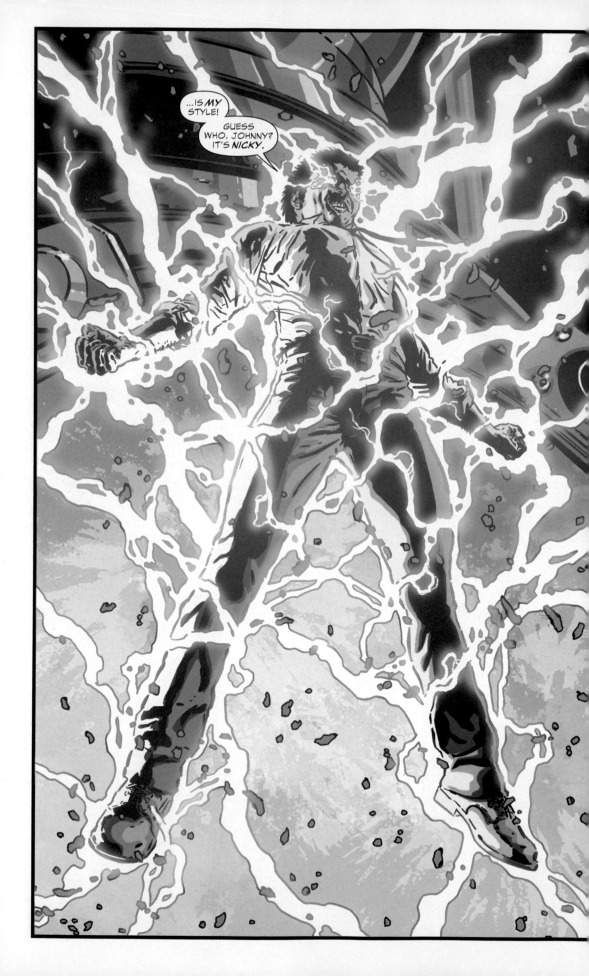

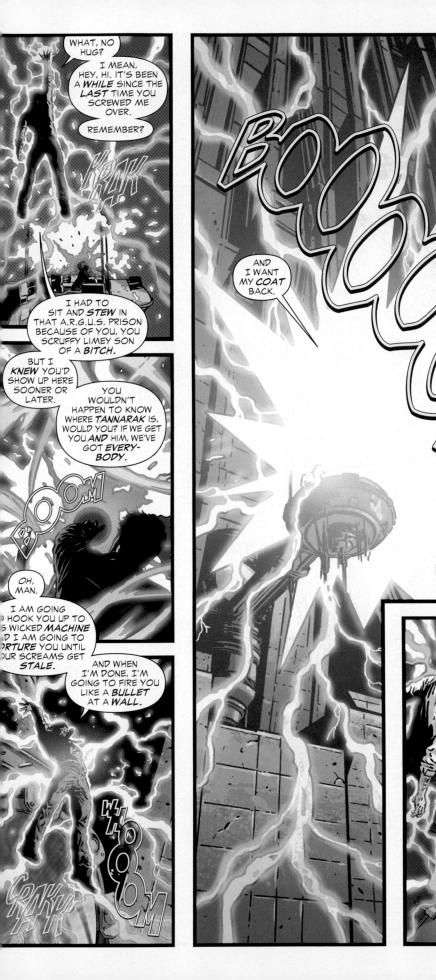

AW, C'MON!

LOOK, JOHN, IT'S *ZEE!* I SAVED YOUR *SPOT* SO YOU COULD *FACE* HER.

SO SHE CAN WATCH WHILE YOU AND I GET IT *ON.*

SHE'S IN A *LOT* OF *PAIN,* JOHN!

YOU BETTER COME OUT AND *HELP* HER!

I'LL TELL YOU WHAT, NICK.

WHY DON'T WE MAKE A *DEAL?* YOU LET ZATANNA AND THE OTHERS GO, AND I WON'T HUMILIATE YOU AGAIN.

NO?

RIGHT, HOW ABOUT THIS? I'LL *JOIN* YOU. WE CAN PUT THE BOOT TO *FAUST* AND RUN THIS THING *TOGETHER* FOR THE SYNDICATE.

YOU, ME, *AND* ZEE.

THAT'S NOT A BAD IDEA, JOHN.

ALL OF US TOGETHER, LIKE THE BAD OLD DAYS.

REALLY? SOUNDS *ACE*, N--

NAH, NOT REALLY.

BOOOM!

HAHA.

THAT WAS A GOOD ONE, JOHN. BUT SERIOUSLY NOW.

ARE YOU REALLY GOING TO MAKE ME THREATEN TO KILL HER? YOU KNOW I HATE A CLICHÉ.

COME OUT, COME--

HUKK

WHAM

NICK.

EVERYTHING YOU *DO* IS A CLICHÉ.

GGH... GGHKK

KAKK

LET'S GET YOU OUT OF THIS THING, YEAH?

ALL RIGHT, ZEE?

NO.

WELL **DONE**, OLD SON.

TALK A GREAT GAME ABOUT HOW WEAK AND PREDICTABLE THESE MAGES ARE, DON'T YOU? AND THEN WHEN IT COMES DOWN TO IT, YOU PLAY THE SILLY **BUGGER**.

I WANT TO SAY THAT FAUST CAST SOME KIND OF **CONFUSION** SPELL SO THAT I WOULDN'T NOTICE HIM. I WANT TO SAY THAT THERE WAS TOO MUCH GOING ON, AND THAT **NOBODY** WOULD'VE BEEN READY FOR HIM.

IT'S ALL NOTHING BUT **EXCUSES**. BLOODY USELESS, IS WHAT IT IS. HERE I AM, EXACTLY WHERE NICK SAID THEY WERE GOING TO PUT ME. AND WHY? BECAUSE I HAD TO RUSH RIGHT IN, EYE ON THE PRIZE, SO SURE I COULD **WIN** THE DAY.

FIRE MYSELF RIGHT AT THE ENEMY LIKE A...

LIKE A **BULLET** AT A WALL.

MY **TAG** AND **TRACK** TELLS ME THAT THE REST OF THE TEAM IS CLOSE. SO AT LEAST THERE'S THAT...

"PEOPLE LIKE TO TALK ABOUT *HELL.* YOU HEAR ABOUT IT ALL THE TIME. 'THIS IS HELL. I'M IN HELL. IT'S ALL GOING TO HELL.'

"BUT THEIR CONCEPT OF IT IS O...HOLLYWOOD. Y'KNOW? SO *BIG 'DGET.* HELL IS WHERE THESE GIANT LSING MACHINES TORTURE PEOPLE.

"AND SCREECHING *MONSTERS* CHEW THEM UP, AND EXCRUCIATING *FLAMES* STRIP THEIR BONES AND WHATNOT.

"THAT'S NOT HELL. THAT'S EARTH. LOOK AROUND. THAT'S WHAT WE DO TO *OURSELVES,* RIGHT *HERE.*

V, MAN. THERE'S THE GHTMARE NURSE.

"I FEEL LIKE I COULD GET *ALONG* WITH HER, Y'KNOW? LIKE SHE'D BE *GREAT* AT PARTIES. WITH HER SEXY, SMOKY VOICE AND THAT *KILLER* SMILE.

"TOO BAD, SO SAD.

"OKAY. THIS RIGHT HERE IS WHAT WE IN THE MYSTIC TRADE LIKE TO CALL A *CRITICAL INEVITABILITY.*

"THAT IS, THIS IS SOMETHING THAT'S *WRITTEN* IN THE BOOK OF DESTINY."

"THERE'S NO WAY *AROUND* IT. THERE ARE NO ALTERNATIVE CHOICES. NO CRUCIAL *DECISIONS* THAT STAVE IT OFF.

"ALL THE VARIABLES IN THE WORLD LEAD TO THIS POINT, AND DIVERGE FROM IT. BUT HERE, THIS:

"THE *GIANT MONSTE*[ ] ATTACKS THE THAUMA[ ] PROJECT. IS IT THE ONE *CRIME SYNDICATE* A[ ] RUNNING FROM?

"WE BLOW ITS HEAD O[ ] DOZENS OF MYSTICS A[ ] *CONSUMED* IN FIRE. MC[ ] OF THOSE GUYS ARE DE[ ] BEFORE THEY HIT THE GROUND. BLOOD PAINT[ ] THE SHATTERED WALLS [ ] THE FIRING CHAMBER.

...HE *POSSIBILITIES* ...TART TO DIVERGE.

"SOMETIMES, *ZATANNA* SCREAMS THROUGH HOT TEARS, KNOWING THAT SHE WAS *PROTECTED* WHILE OTHERS WERE ALLOWED TO DIE.

"AND SOMEONE WALKS TOWARDS HER DRAGGING A *BODY.*

"AND SHE SWEARS THAT SHE'LL LIVE TO SEE THEM *PAY.*

"AND AFTER THAT, THE *FUTURE* GETS HAZY. TOO MANY POSSIBILITIES."

DAMN.

"D'YOU KNOW WHAT *HELL* LOOKS LIKE, JOHN?"

I'M NOT BEING *METAPHORICAL* HERE.

I'M ASKING IF YOU'VE *SEEN* HELL.

I HAVE.

"I DIED AND *WENT* THERE.

"BROTHER, I SCREAMED A THE WAY DOWN. BEGGING AND *CRYING* AND ALL TH SHAMEFUL CRAP YOU SWE YOU'LL *NEVER* DO."

ANYWAY, HELL. IT LOOKS LIKE...

...WELL, YOU'RE PROBABLY PICTURING LIKE AN ABANDONED *HOSPITAL* OR A BURNED-OUT *SLAUGHTERHOUSE*, RIGHT?

SOMETHING THAT MAKES YOU *UNCOMFORTABLE.* THE LITTLE ROOM THAT GUY ON YOUR *STREET* USED TO TAKE YOU TO WHEN NOBODY WAS AROUND.

YOU'RE NOT EVEN *CLOSE.*

HELL ISN'T ABOUT MAKING YOU *SQUIRM.* IT'S HUGE AND *IMPERSONAL* AND *BLANK.*

IT'S WHERE YOU REALIZE THAT HOW YOU *FEEL* MEANS *NOTHING* AND YOU *ARE NOTHING.* YOU CAN'T *IMAGINE* HOW AWFUL IT IS.

YOU'LL SEE.

"ARE YOU ENJOYING YOURSELF

"ATTABOY, JOHNNY...

"GOT YOURSELF DOWN OFF THAT MACHINE WITH *ZATARA'S* ESCAPE.

"HOW YA FEELIN'? WEAK? GOT A BAD CASE OF THE *SHAKES*?

"WE *DID* PUMP YOU FULL OF *SEDATIVES* AND PSYCHO-ACTIVE *CONFUSION* SPELLS UP ON THAT WHEEL.

NOT THAT IT SHOULD SLOW YOU DOWN *THAT* MUCH, RIGHT?

"I MEAN, YOU AND ME, WE USED TO CALL THAT MIX *'SATURDAY NIGHT.'"*

HEY.

...I...I THOUGHT ONLY *TRUE DRUIDS* COULD CAST THE WOOD WALK LIKE THAT, ANYWAY.

YEAH? WELL, I'VE GOT DRUID BLOOD, ME. HAVE DONE EVER SINCE I *WON* A PINT OF IT OFF OF ONE IN A *VERY* ENJOYABLE GAME OF CHANCE.

WHY DON'T YOU JUST LET ZATANNA GO *YOUR-SELF*, NICKY? WHY FREE *ME* INSTEAD? WHY SET UP THIS *DUEL*?

CRACK

OUGH!

OH, NO...

PAT

PAT

CONSTANTINE # 7 LAYOUT COVER B

Issue #7 cover layouts by Eddy Barrows

CONSTANTINE #7 LAYOUT COVER (C)

CONSTANTINE #7 LAYOUT COVER (D)

CONSTANTINE #8 LAYOUT COVER

CONSTANTINE #8 LAYOUT COVER (B)

CONSTANTINE #8 LAYOUT COVER (C)

Issue #12 cover sketches and pencils by Howard Porter

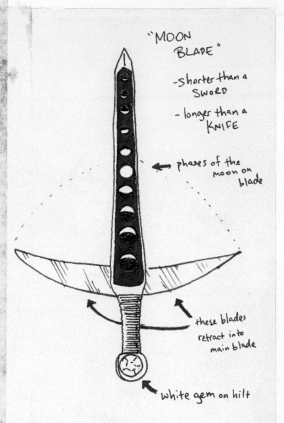

"MOON BLADE"

- shorter than a SWORD

- longer than a KNIFE

← phases of the moon on blade

these blades retract into main blade

← white gem on hilt

Designs by editor Brian Cunningham and assistant editor Kate Stewart

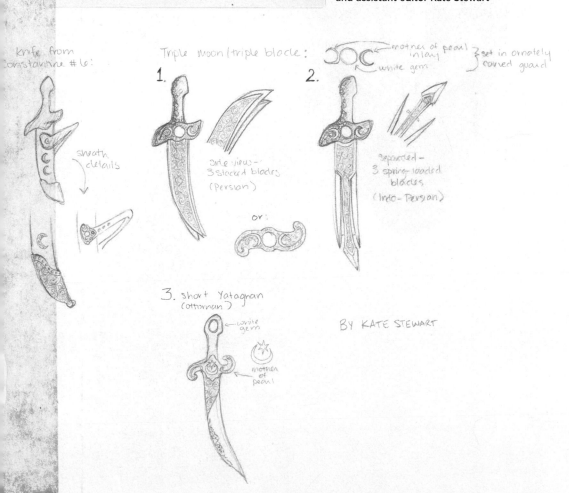

knife from Constantine #6:

sheath details ↓

Triple moon / triple blade:

1.

Side view – 3 stacked blades (Persian)

or:

2.

mother of pearl inlay

white gem

set in ornately carved guard

separated – 3 spring-loaded blades (Indo-Persian)

3. short Yataghan (ottoman)

← white gem

mother of pearl

BY KATE STEWART

Design by Ray Fawkes

- Sparkles & shines in open air, surrounded by tiny "stars"

- Blade looks normal inside but glows brightly in moonlight
- Maybe it grows to match the moon phase (so it's a short dagger in new moo & a full sword i for moon)?

"Moons" in hilt retract

bright gem in hilt (white) that leaves a light trail as the blade moves